Microchemical Methods for the Identification of Lichens

A. Orange, P.W. James and F. J. White

British Lichen Society

2010

Reprinted 2013

ISBN 978 0 9540418 9 2

CONTENTS

1. INTRODUCTION

Lichens are remarkable for their production of a wide range of secondary products, and for the relative ease with which these products can be studied and used to provide taxonomic information. This book aims to provide a practical guide to the identification of lichen substances, using methods that are within the scope of most lichen taxonomists. It is a revised and updated version of A New Guide to Microchemical Techniques for the Identification of Lichen Substances (White & James 1985), itself based on an earlier publication (Walker & James 1980).

The chemical methods used by lichenologists vary from extremely cheap and simple to expensive and sophisticated. Many excellent lichenologists work with at most four simple reagents, known by the symbols K, C, PD and I. The beginner to lichenology should not be discouraged by the amount of detail in this book: Table 1 provides a summary of a few basic tests that can be used by all lichenologists. The table will also guide the beginner to the relevant section of text which gives more details. Some household bleach, a solution of potassium hydroxide and a hand lens are quite sufficient with which to begin the study of lichens!

Spot tests and other methods using simple reagents can be used by any lichenologist. Microcrystallization is a simple method that has been largely superseded by thin-layer chromatography (TLC), but which is still the simplest method of separating substances in a few groups of related species (see Section 6). The method is also of historical interest in the development of lichen chemotaxonomy. Thin-layer chromatography is routinely used in the major herbaria; it is a sensitive but relatively inexpensive method which is simple to use, although for safety reasons it requires basic laboratory facilities such as a fume cupboard and secure storage for chemicals (see Section 9).

Sophisticated methods such as mass spectrometry, NMR (nuclear magnetic resonance) spectroscopy and high performance liquid chromatography (HPLC) are important for isolation and identification of lichen substances, but these methods are the province of the specialist organic chemist, and are outside the scope of this book. Some of these methods are mentioned briefly by Huneck & Yoshimura (1996) and Elix & Stocker-Wörgötter (2008), where additional references can be found. Fortunately, the substances identified by these methods can be demonstrated by simpler procedures that are available to most taxonomists.

Many of the substances mentioned in this book are hazardous. Some of the procedures, including thin-layer chromatography, must not be used outside the laboratory. A few reagents, mentioned for their intrinsic interest or for the sake of completeness, should be handled only by experienced chemists. Although some hazards are mentioned in the text or in Section 11, the safe storage, handling, use and disposal of chemicals is outside the scope of this book. It is the responsibility of each individual to evaluate the risks associated with each procedure and to take appropriate precautions.

Lichen names used in this book follow Smith *et al.* (2009) for species that occur in the British Isles, except where indicated. With a few exceptions, names of lichen substances follow Huneck & Yoshimura (1996).

A note on measures: some formulae published by lichenologists are rather imprecise. The phrase '50% nitric acid', used by a lichenologist, is usually meant to specify a mixture of equal volumes of 'concentrated' nitric acid and water, but this phrase would have a different meaning for a chemist. In this book such phrases have been retained, but where possible the formula has been defined precisely.

1.1. Lichen substances

The substances covered in this book include a wide range of compounds. The most characteristic lichen substances are secondary metabolites, which are typically deposited on the outside of the cell walls, but some primary metabolites are included, namely polysaccharides which are found in the cell wall. Readable general accounts of lichen substances include Elix & Stocker-Wörgötter (2008), Hawksworth & Hill (1984), and Hale (1983). More specialised accounts include Huneck (1973, 1984), Elix *et al.* (1984) and Culberson (1969). Specialised accounts with the emphasis on biosynthesis include Culberson & Elix (1989) and Mosbach (1973). Publications which list all lichen substances known at the time are Huneck & Yoshimura (1996), and the earlier volumes of Culberson (1969), Culberson (1970), and Culberson *et al.* (1977). Smith *et al.* (2009) is an important source of chemical information on British and Irish species.

1.2. Lichen chemotaxonomy

At least 60% of British lichens have identifiable secondary compounds, and this is particularly important in certain genera (e.g. *Bryoria, Lepraria* and *Usnea*), where morphological characters may not always be easy to interpret.

In many lichens, the chemical substances that they contain are more or less constant for that species. However, variation in chemistry is not uncommon within a species or a group of related species. Thus a single species may contain two or more 'chemical races' that differ only in their main chemical constituents. Other chemicals known as 'accessory substances' may also occur; by definition these are not constantly present in a species or chemical race. They are often indicated in the literature by a '±' sign. Note, however, that in biochemical discussions the term 'accessory substances' is used for those on the same biosynthetic pathway. Whether a chemical is considered to be accessory or not will often depend on the sensitivity of the method of analysis used and/or the quantities present in the material to be tested.

A number of rather similar terms are used to describe the chemical variation seen in lichens. Groups of individuals which differ from each other in chemistry, whatever the taxonomic treatment applied to them, are referred to as chemical races (also termed chemical strains or chemodemes). The term chemotype is typically used for chemically differing entities within a species, of no or of unknown taxonomic significance. Sometimes two chemical races differ in the possession of chemicals which are on the same biosynthetic pathway, and these are often assumed to be of less significance than races which differ in chemicals on different pathways. Two chemical races may contain the same suite of compounds but in different proportions. These are likely to be a group of compounds on the same biosynthetic pathway, known as a chemosyndrome, and this type of chemical variation is thus known as chemosyndromic. Occasionally an individual lichen may occur which lacks a substance (a 'lichen acid') which is normally present in that species; these are often termed acid-deficient individuals.

The taxonomic treatment of chemical variation in lichens remains controversial. Generally, however, chemical races are not given the status of species unless the chemical variation is also accompanied by (sometimes subtle) morphological differences. Hawksworth (1976) provides a review of this topic; see also Brodo (1986), Egan (1986), Poelt & Leuckert (1993) and Rogers (1989).

1.3. Technique ethics

Chemical analysis is a destructive technique. Extreme care should always be taken in the handling of herbarium material when any of the microchemical analyses outlined below are undertaken. Specimens may be fragmentary, and if an analysis is undertaken, only the smallest amount should be tested. Type specimens should *only* be examined when a serious taxonomic revision is being undertaken and never during routine studies; type material which is fragmentary or scanty should not be tested. All thallus spot tests should be undertaken on a small fragment removed from the main specimen, and should be discarded after testing. Care should be taken neither to deface the specimen nor to allow any chemical reagents to come into contact with either the material, herbarium sheets or books. Specimens in public herbaria are irreplaceable and must be handled with extreme care. Full details of results obtained, including the method of analysis, date, and the name of the identifier, should always be appended to the collection using a suitable label with permanent ink. Negative results (such as absence of fatty acids or absence of chloroatranorin in TLC) should be mentioned, in cases where it would not be clear whether these have been tested for or not. This procedure will avoid unneccessary duplication of analyses and further depletion of critical material. Fragments of macrolichens (such as podetia of *Cladonia*) are not altered morphologically by extraction with acetone, and can be placed in a suitably labelled micropacket within the main herbarium packet, cross-referenced to the analysis slip.

In the field, only the smallest amount of reagent should be added to the lichen to be tested, as the reagent is likely to kill the area tested. It is often sufficient to touch a thallus with the moistened tip of a pipette and observe the reaction with a handlens.

1.4. General methods

Secondary metabolites in lichens are accumulated on the surface of the fungal hyphae and may be either widely dispersed or strictly confined to specific tissues. Atranorin, and pigments such as usnic acid, are often sited in the thallus cortex, whilst most colourless substances (mainly depsides and depsidones) tend to be confined within the medulla and algal layer of the thallus. The overall chemical complement of the thallus remains the same throughout the life of an individual specimen, but apothecia, and sometimes soralia, pycnidia, pseudocyphellae and cephalodia, may have a different or additional chemistry from that of the parent vegetative thallus. In a few cases, a compound may only be produced in response to an environmental factor, such as the red spots containing rhodocladonic acid on the squamules of *Cladonia norvegica*, formed in response to feeding by mites. Consequently, it is important to note the tissue which is analyzed or tested, and to ensure that guidelines given in identification keys are followed to ensure that the correct tissue is being tested. Similarly, the localisation of pigments in microscopic preparations of ascomata should be carefully recorded. In general, the healthy, growing portions of thalli or podetia should be selected for TLC, as these are likely to have a greater concentration of lichen substances.

It is possible to use the same material for more than one method. Part of an extract for TLC can also be spotted onto a slide for a microcrystal test. When mixed collections are suspected, the same individual can be analysed by different methods, for instance a single podetium of *Cladonia* can be divided (preferably by a longitudinal cut) into two or more pieces for spot tests and TLC. Material can be scraped from TLC plates (before heating) and extracted with acetone for spot tests or microcrystal tests.

It is important that the material to be tested is uniform. The presence of other species will cause contamination and give false results. It is easy to overlook contaminants especially when testing crustose species. Mixed collections of fruticose species (such as *Cladonia* and *Usnea*) are frequent, and only one podetium or thallus should be analyzed at a time.

The appearance of a lichen sometimes provides clues to the chemicals which it contains. Pigments are striking and taxonomically important, and may belong to one of several classes of compounds (see Section 3). After a few years storage in the herbarium, the presence of other chemicals may be apparent: alectorialic acid turns specimens and herbarium packets a pinkish brown colour (e.g. *Alectoria nigricans*, *Buellia pulverea*). Some lichens develop a pale bloom of fine crystals over the surface during storage (e.g. *Cladonia diversa*, *Megalospora tuberculosa*); this is sometimes attributed to the presence of terpenoids, but many species containing terpenoids do not develop such a bloom. Grey species which contain norstictic acid turn a dull yellowish colour. Even taste is occasionally used as a taxonomic character. The very bitter taste of the soralia of *Pertusaria amara* is due to picrolichenic acid, and is well known as a field character which distinguishes this species from *P.*

albescens. The bitter taste of fumarprotocetraric acid was formerly used to differentiate *Cladonia* species, but the reagent PD is a much more reliable indicator of this substance.

2. SPOT TESTS AND OTHER CHEMICAL REACTIONS

Spot tests for colour reactions of lichen tissues are universally used as a rapid, nonspecific, means for detecting the presence of certain unspecified lichen substances. An important feature of these tests is that they are mostly convenient and simple to perform, even under field conditions, especially in those circumstances (e.g. in churchyards), where material cannot conveniently be collected. However, it is important that these simple tests are regarded as only a preliminary step in the process of identification of the lichen or its substances. In order to identify a particular lichen substance it will always be necessary to use more sensitive tests, such as thin-layer chromatography, as described below. As a precaution it should be noted that there have been many instances where misinterpretation of spot tests has led to errors in determination. Examples of particular pitfalls and possible reasons for the more frequent misinterpretations are given below.

Although spot tests are simple, they can be very useful in detecting the presence and determining the localization of substances; they may also give useful pointers to identification of substances observed in TLC. For these reasons, it is worthwhile carrying out spot tests with care.

2.1. Reagents

Commonly used reagents:

1. Potassium hydroxide solution (K)
     potassium hydroxide   10 g
     distilled water   100 ml

Other concentrations (such as 20-35%) are commonly quoted in the literature, but the 10% solution above appears to be adequate. The solution absorbs carbon dioxide from the air and gradually becomes ineffective; it should be replaced when it becomes cloudy. Sodium hydroxide (caustic soda) can be used as a substitute.

2. Sodium hypochlorite solution (C)
Undiluted liquid household bleach can be a convenient source, but Dobson (2004) pointed out that many brands now contain additional substances, which may produce false reactions in KC or CK tests. Test the bleach on the medulla of *Parmelia saxatilis* or *P. sulcata*; there should be no reaction. A positive, orange reaction indicates that the bleach contains substances in addition to sodium hypochlorite. A good source is Milton Sterilising Fluid, marketed for sterilising baby equipment, and said to contain 2% w/w sodium hypochlorite. For laboratory use, it is convenient to store C in the large original container, removing the solution with a glass rod when needed. For field use it can be transported in a dropper bottle, but should be replaced frequently as the solution decomposes readily; the solution should be replaced as soon as it does not smell strongly of chlorine.

3. *para*-Phenylenediamine (1,4-phenylenediamine) (PD)
In the laboratory, use two or three crystals freshly dissolved in a few drops of ethanol (industrial methylated spirit) in a watch glass. This evaporates rapidly, but can be remoistened with additional drops of ethanol. An ethanolic solution rapidly turns brown due to oxidation of the PD. The residue remaining at the end of an identification session should be discarded. PD crystals left outside the bottle will deteriorate and give false results. Although the watch glass can be stored in a petri dish until needed again, PD will diffuse out from the dish, as is shown by irremoveable brown stains which will appear on adjacent paper or woodwork.

Steiner's solution provides a stable PD solution which can be stored for a few months:

para-phenylenediamine	1 g
sodium sulphite	10 g
detergent (e.g. household washing up liquid)	*c.* 0.5 ml
distilled water	100 ml.

Para-phenylenediamine is toxic and is a suspected carcinogen which should be handled with great care (Dobson 2001). For this reason, Steiner's solution is not particularly recommended, as contamination may occur during handling, and the oxidised solution will eventually require disposal. Unless PD is needed in the field for a specific project, it is best to use it only in the laboratory. Minute amounts of PD spilt onto paper or books will cause unsightly and indelible brown stains.

Kirschbaum & Wirth (1995) suggested a related chemical, *N, N*-diethyl-1,4-phenylenediamine sulphate ('Merck Colour Developer 1'), as a substitute for PD. It was said to give similar results, but reactions were slower and paler than with PD. A stable solution was recommended, comprising 3 g of this chemical dissolved in a solution of 10 g of anhydrous sodium sulphite in 100 ml distilled water, with 1 ml of washing up liquid added.

Infrequently used reagents:

4. Barium hydroxide ($Ba(OH)_2$)
        An approximately 10% solution in water.
An acetone extract on filter paper gives a violet colour with diploschistesic acid; this occurs together with lecanoric acid in some chemotypes of *Diploschistes* spp., both substances are C + red.

5. Barium peroxide (BaO_2) (Huneck & Yoshimura 1996)
        Saturated solution in water.
Gives a lemon yellow colour with olivetoric acid, turning to green after some minutes. Control: *Pseudevernia furfuracea* var. *ceratea*.

6. Ferric chloride ($FeCl_3$) (Iron (III) chloride)
        A 1% w/v solution in ethanol (Industrial Methylated Spirit).
This reagent provides a test for phenolic groups (shades of grey, blue, brown, red or violet), and thus reacts with a large number of lichen secondary metabolites. Its routine use is limited, but the different shades of colour produced when applied to acetone extracts could be investigated as a means of distinguishing certain species when other spot tests are negative.

7. Alkaline potassium ferricyanide solution (Archer 1984)

potassium ferricyanide ($K_3Fe(CN)_6$)	0.4 g
potassium hydroxide (KOH)	4 g
Make up to 100 ml with distilled water.	

To detect didymic acid when occurring with barbatic acid, which has a similar R_f. The original formula used NaOH instead of KOH.

8. Dimroth's reagent (Santesson 1968)

boric acid	10 g
acetic anhydride	100 ml

Add the boric acid in small amounts to 100 ml of hot (100° C) acetic anhydride and allow to cool. Place a drop of an acetone extract of lichen on filter paper and allow to dry. Add reagent and observe under long-wave UV. Xanthones give a brilliant yellow fluorescence lasting for at least one minute. The reagent can also be added to the intact lichen. The reaction depends on the presence of a hydroxyl group in the 1 position. The reaction is also obtained with chromones such as sordidone. Acetic anhydride is hazardous, and this test is not recommended for routine use.

TABLE 1. SUMMARY OF SIMPLE LICHEN TESTS

Many identification keys use the results of some very simple tests which are suitable for use by beginners to lichenology. These tests are summarized here. See the text for more details: Section 2 for K, C and PD, Section 4.1 and 4.2 for simple use of I, Section 8 for UV.

Reagents/ tests	Formula	Positive reactions	Examples (use these species to test that the reagent is working)	Notes
K	10% solution of potassium hydroxide in water; replace when old or cloudy.	yellow, red (dirty yellow due merely to clearing effect is negative); some turn slowly red forming microscopic crystals	*Phlyctis argena* (red with crystals), *Pertusaria corallina* (bright yellow), *Cladonia polydactyla* (yellow), *Xanthoria parietina* (red-purple)	May help to apply K, then after a while draw solution onto filter paper to help see pale reactions.
C	sodium hypochlorite solution (use a suitable household bleach); replace frequently	pink, red, orange (rarely green)	*Ochrolechia androgyna*, *Melanelixia subaurifera* (medulla pink or red)	Reactions often fleeting, only a second or two!
KC	K followed by C on the same fragment	pink, red, rarely violet	*Hypogymnia physodes* (medulla red), *Pertusaria amara* (soralia violet)	May help to apply K, then draw solution onto filter paper, add C to paper.
PD	a few crystals dissolved in alcohol (Industrial Methylated Spirit) in a watch glass	yellow, orange, red	*Parmelia sulcata*, *Hypogymnia physodes* (medulla orange in both), *Cladonia pyxidata* (orange-red)	PD is toxic and may cause cancer! Reactions may be slow (1-2 minutes).
I	0.5 g iodine, 1.5 g potassium iodide, dissolved in 100 ml water	blue, violet, rarely red	*Porpidia tuberculosa*, *Lecidea lactea* (medulla violet in both)	Pretreatment with K may help. I is not used in the field.
UV	long-wave ultra-violet (350 nm) from mains or portable lamp	fluorescence, usually white, bluish or orange	*Cladonia portentosa*, *C. squamosa* (whitish)	Cortex may mask fluorescence, try abrading the surface.

IN THE FIELD:
- Carry reagents K and C in stout brown glass dropper bottles.
- Do not use PD in the field as it is hazardous; I is not used in the field.
- Add a small drop of reagent to the lichen – use as little as possible as it will kill the parts it touches.
- Observe with a hand-lens if possible; reactions may be fleeting – observe while testing, or immediately afterwards!
- Try scraping very dark thalli to reveal paler tissues within.
- When using UV, shade the lichen from daylight.

IN THE LABORATORY:
- Add a small drop of reagent to a small piece removed from the rest of the lichen (to avoid ruining the whole specimen).
- Watch the test with a dissecting microscope if possible.
- Reactions may be fleeting – observe while testing!
- Try scraping or sectioning very dark dark thalli to reveal paler tissues.
- Add I to sections or squashes – it is usually necessary to use a high power microscope.
- Use UV lamp in a darkened room.

10

2.2. Methods of testing

1. Direct

In the laboratory, tests should be carried out on a fragment of lichen separated from the rest of the specimen, and the fragment discarded following testing. Reagents can be applied directly to the lichen using a glass rod or capillary tube. In the field a small, strong, brown glass dropper bottle (available from pharmacists) is suitable for transporting reagents. Testing in the field can be a great help in distinguishing similar species and confirming identifications. All serious lichenologists should be prepared to carry K and C in the field. In general, a more sensitive reaction is obtained when small quantities of reagent are used.

Tests should be carried out under a hand-lens (×10), or preferably a binocular microscope. For tests involving examination of the medulla a small area of the overlying cortex should first be removed using a razor blade. When small fragments are to be tested, it is convenient to place a small drop of reagent on a microscope slide, and to push the fragment into it using forceps. In the laboratory it is often convenient to prepare sections of the lichen thallus or ascoma. These can be placed on a microscope slide and viewed under a binocular microscope and wetted with a small drop of reagent. In this way information on the localization of substances in different tissues may be obtained.

2. Indirect

In some lichens colour reactions may be masked by dark pigments or by a spongy texture, or the reactions may be faint or fleeting. In these cases it is useful to use filter paper as a base for the reaction. There are several ways of doing this:

a. Extraction with acetone

A piece of filter paper is folded cross-wise so as to form a slight depression in the centre. Small fragments of lichen are placed in the centre of the filter paper. Holding the paper over a hotplate (but not in direct contact), approximately 6 drops of acetone are added one at a time, allowing each drop to dry before adding the next. The paper is allowed to dry, and the fragments of lichen are brushed away. Spot tests can be carried out on the ring of extracted substances on the filter paper.

A small refinement of this method is to extract lichen fragments in one or two drops of acetone in a small test tube. The extract is drawn up in a capillary tube and added a small amount at a time to the centre of a small pencil ring drawn onto a piece of filter paper, allowing each application to dry before adding the next. This gives a more concentrated spot of substances. The area of the pencil ring can be cut into 3 or more fragments and each tested separately.

b. Use of filter paper for the KC and CK reactions (see Section 2.3).

Apply the first reagent to the thallus and then absorb it onto the corner of a piece of filter paper. Add a spot of the second reagent onto the filter paper to produce a reaction. Note that KC and CK reactions are nearly always fleeting.

c. Use of Steiner's Solution in *Bryoria* (Brodo & Hawksworth 1977)

This is a specialized technique developed for *Bryoria* filaments. Filaments are placed on a square of filter paper on a glass slide and flooded with 2-3 drops of Steiner's Solution (stable PD reagent, see Section 2.1). Colour produced will diffuse out of the thallus and spread onto the paper. Excessive quantities of reagent should be avoided as this causes over-dilution. This method is also used to distinguish which parts of the thallus, e.g. soralia or layers of the cortex, is responsible for the reaction. The solution also makes the filament transparent so that any positive colour reaction in the inner cortex or medulla can be seen through the cortex and will not diffuse out into the filter paper.

3. Microscope preparations

If the reactions produced by spot tests of intact thallus are uncertain, it is advisable to make a squash or thin section of the lichen tissue to observe under the microscope. The tissue is mounted in a minimal amount of water, and the appropriate reagent is drawn under the coverslip. The tissue should be observed under low power while the reagent is drawn under, particularly for fleeting reactions such as those caused by C. Reactions with C can often be observed as a coloured front moving across the tissue section, with the colour rapidly fading in its wake. In other cases it may be visible as a fleeting reddish colouration surrounding thallus fragments. Some reactions must be observed under the microscope, for instance the production of crystals caused by the reaction of K and norstictic acid, the confluentic acid test (see below), and all tests involving iodine (see Section 4).

Many colours and reactions are obscured by the yellowish illumination given by most light bulbs, and it is recommended that the microscope be fitted with a 'daylight bulb' or a blue filter.

CAUTION: reagents (particularly K and nitric acid) may cause damage to microscope objectives, and on no account should come into direct contact with the lens. For this reason only the low power objective should be used, and the slide should not be left on the microscope stage for longer than is necessary.

2.3. Tests

K

Produces yellow to red reactions with a range of substances, including certain depsides, depsidones, and chromones. Forms a precipitate of red needle-like crystals (low power of microscope) with norstictic acid (allow at least 20 seconds for reaction to begin). Differentiates between pigments of quinone type (blue to red or purple reactions) and pulvinic acid derivatives (no reaction). Some K + yellow reactions are rather faint. Care should be taken to avoid recording a misleading K + yellow reaction which can be produced 5 to 10 seconds after application; this is due to the clearing effect of K on the normally opaque thallus cortex, allowing the colour of the underlying algae to be seen. The K reaction with protocetraric and fumarprotocetraric acids is negative, but when the substance is abundant it can give dull yellowish to brownish red colours, which can be misleading. The yellow colour of a positive K reaction may be more easily seen by drawing up the reagent from the lichen surface onto filter paper (if paper other than filter paper is used, ensure that the paper itself does not turn yellow with K).

Examples of species which can be used as test controls for K include *Cladonia polydactyla* (yellow-orange), *Pertusaria pseudocorallina* or *Phlyctis argena* (yellow changing to red with crystals), and *Caloplaca* and *Xanthoria* species (purple). Examples of K + substances are shown in Table 2.

C

Gives orange or red reactions with some depsides, xanthones and others, and green reactions with some dibenzofuranes, such as strepsilin in *Cladonia strepsilis*. The reactions are often fleeting, lasting only for a second or two. Some faint reactions are better observed using the KC test. The orange or red reactions occur in substances which have two free hydroxyl groups in *meta*-position (arrowed in Fig. 1), unless a –CHO or –CO$_2$H group is substituted between the hydroxyl groups. Reactions with dibenzofuranes other than strepsilin are difficult to demonstrate.

Examples of species which can be used as test controls to assess the strength of C include: *Ochrolechia androgyna* and *O. tartarea* (orange-red due to gyrophoric acid) or the medulla of *Melanelixia fuliginosa* or *M. subaurifera* (red due to lecanoric acid). Examples of C + substances are shown in Table 3.

KC

In this test K is added to the material to be tested, quickly followed by C. Positive reactions are red, rarely violet or yellow. Some compounds which show weak reactions with C show stronger reactions with KC, but some KC + compounds are C −. Reactions are often fleeting.

K hydrolyses the ester linkage (-CO-O-) in depsides and depsidones, producing a free OH group; if this is located *meta* to another hydroxyl group then a coloured reaction can take place with C.

Examples of species which can be used as test controls include *Hypogymnia physodes* and *Cetrelia olivetorum* (race) where the medulla reacts KC + rose red, and the soralia of *Pertusaria amara* (KC + violet). Examples of KC + substances are shown in Table 4.

CK
This test is not commonly used as a standard method. In this test C is added to the material, followed by K. Reacts orange with barbatic acid (*Cladonia floerkeana*), and yellow-orange with diffractaic acid (*Alectoria ochroleuca*, *Usnea ceratina*).

PD
Causes a yellow to red reaction with aromatic lichen substances containing an aldehyde (CHO) group. The full colour may take a minute or two to develop. This reagent also causes a striking but misleading blue reaction when mixed with traces of C.

Examples of species which can be used as test controls include *Cladonia pyxidata* (red), *Schismatomma niveum* (orange), *Parmelia saxatilis* and *P. sulcata* (medulla yellow to red). Examples of PD + substances are shown in Table 5.

KOH confluentic acid test (Fryday 1992a)
Mount a section or small fragment of tissue in water on a microscope slide, apply a coverslip, then draw K into the preparation. After a few seconds, minute droplets issues from the tissue, forming a dull-coloured halo. The droplets comprise 4-O-methylolivetonide (*para*-methyletherolivetonide), which is insoluble in K, and which is produced by hydrolysis of confluentic acid by K (Fryday 1992b).

Particularly useful in the genus *Porpidia*, to distinguish species containing confluentic acid (e.g. *P. cinereoatra*, *P. speirea* and *P. tuberculosa*) from those without (including *P. contraponenda*, *P. macrocarpa*, and also *P. platycarpoides* which is K + red with crystals), and for distinguishing *Lecidea confluens* and *L. lapicida*.

A solution of sodium hydroxide will also produces some droplets, but these are rapidly replaced by needle-like crystals.

Alkaline potassium ferricyanide test for didymic acid (Archer 1984)
Apply an acetone extract of the lichen onto filter paper and allow to dry. Add a drop of alkaline potassium ferricyanide. A blue-violet colour which lasts for several minutes indicates the presence of the dibenzofurane didymic acid. The test can be used to distinguish *Cladonia* chemotypes containing thamnolic, barbatic and didymic acids from those containing only thamnolic and barbatic acids, and to detect the presence of didymic acid in some chemotypes of *Cladonia incrassata*.

Acetone extracts of *Cladonia strepsilis* (containing the dibenzofurane strepsilin) give a very faint and fleeting bluish reaction lasting only a second or so, which is unlikely to be confused with the distinct and more persistent reaction with didymic acid.

C test for didymic acid (Asahina 1939)
This test may be useful when didymic acid is likely to be present in a sample, but potassium ferricyanide is not available. Extract the lichen fragment in acetone on a microscope slide, or apply an acetone extract from a test tube onto a slide by means of a capillary tube. Observing with a dissecting microscope, apply a small drop of C to the residue. Then apply a small drop of alcohol (IMS) nearby, so that the alcohol spreads and mixes with the drop of C. If didymic acid is present, the residue turns a dull green. Strepsilin also causes a coloured reaction, but in this case the residue on the slide reacts a distinct C + blue-green, without the need for addition of alcohol.

13

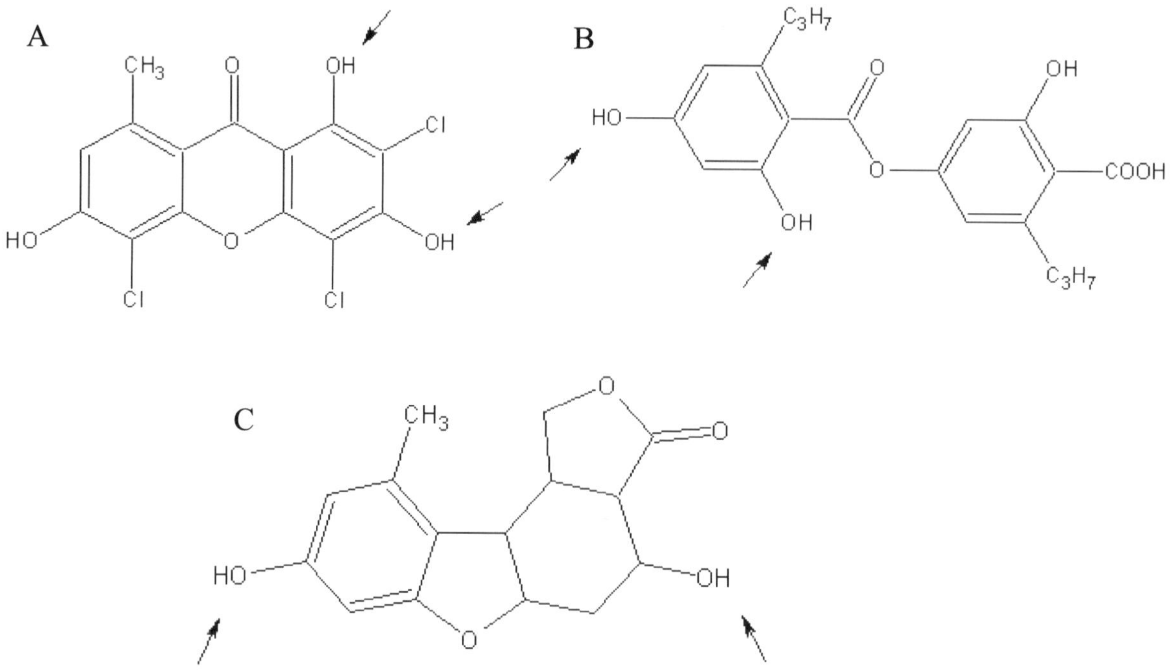

FIG. 1. Three compounds which produce a colour reaction with C. A, arthothelin, B, nordivaricatic acid, C, strepsilin. Hydroxyl groups which are responsible for the reaction are arrowed.

K test for polyporic acid

Polyporic acid is rare in lichens, and is difficult to identify using TLC, as it produces a dull-coloured streaking with no definite R_f.

A section of thallus is placed in a drop of K on a microscope slide. Polyporic acid initially dissolves to form a violet solution, but rapidly recrystallizes as large violet crystals. The reaction can be seen under the dissecting microscope or under a high power microscope. Other quinones which dissolve to form purple or violet solutions in K do not recrystallize in this way. Allow a minute or two for the test to work. This test works well with *Pseudocyphellaria colensoi* (Australasia), which contains large quantities of polyporic acid as brownish deposits; under the dissecting microscope the violet crystals are conspicuous against the yellow lichen tissue. Polyporic acid is also reported from *P. coronata* (Australasia), but here the test is complicated by the presence of a K + purple to red substance which goes into solution. The fruit body of the non-lichenized polypore *Hapalopilus nidulans* is a good control.

2.4. Problems with spot tests

Failure to obtain or observe an anticipated positive result may be due to one of the following causes:

a. Ageing solutions

Reagents deteriorate during storage and must be checked at frequent intervals using some of the test species of known chemical composition suggested above. If these species give the correct colour and intensity of reaction, it indicates that the reagent is still in good condition.

b. Low concentration of lichen substances

Sometimes the concentration of substances is insufficient to produce a convincing colour reaction. Filter paper methods are more sensitive than whole-thallus methods, but if the reaction is still unconvincing then more sensitive methods such as TLC must be used.

c. Reaction time

14

Reactions with C and KC are nearly always fleeting, taking place within a second of application of the reagent and soon fading, and are consequently often missed. The thallus should be carefully observed under a lens, or preferably a binocular microscope during application of the reagent. Conversely, PD may take up to 30 seconds or more to react, and the colour may change or intensify after a short time lapse of about one minute. It may be necessary to confirm certain reactions using a microscope preparation on a slide.

d. Localisation of lichen substances
General tests involving non-specific areas of the thallus should be carried out on young, actively growing parts, such as lobe and branch tips. However, substances are frequently localised within specific areas of the thallus and in certain species a particular substance may only be present in either the cortex, medulla, soralia, pycnidia, apothecial margin or disc. Care must be taken when using identification keys to ensure that the correct organ or area is tested; sectioning of the material and examination under a microsope may sometimes be necessary.

e. Colour of thallus
Colour reactions can often be overlooked in the case of dark thalli. In this case use the indirect methods of testing described in Section 2.2.

f. Presence of additional substances, the reactions of which may mask weaker reactions due to other substances.

TABLE 2. Examples of lichen substances causing coloured reactions with K.			
substance	chemical class	reaction	examples
parietin	anthraquinone	red-purple	*Xanthoria parietina*
rhodocladonic acid*	naphthaquinone	dark red	*Cladonia floerkeana* (apothecia)
skyrin*	bis-anthraquinone	dark red	*Phaeophyscia orbicularis*
haemoventosin*	naphthaquinone	blue then violet	*Ophioparma ventosa* (apothecia)
lepraric acid	chromome	lemon yellow	*Lecanactis latebrarum, L. subabietina* (pycnidial pruina)
siphulin	chromome	dull orange	*Siphula ceratites*
atranorin	didepside	yellow	*Cladonia subcervicornis*
baeomycesic acid	didepside	yellow	*Baeomyces roseus*
thamnolic acid	didepside	bright yellow	*Cladonia polydactyla, Pertusaria corallina*
norstictic acid	depsidone	yellow then red, with crystals	*Pertusaria pseudocorallina, Phlyctis argena*
stictic acid	depsidone	yellow	*Parmotrema perlatum, Usnea flammea*
salazinic acid	depsidone	yellow, then orange to red, no crystals	*Parmotrema reticulatum, Usnea filipendula*
*Note that these substances (quinones) are already coloured.			

15

TABLE 3. Examples of substances causing coloured reactions with C.

substance	chemical class	reaction	examples
siphulin	chromone	violet-pink, then yellowish orange	*Siphula ceratites*
arthothelin	xanthone	orange	*Buellia ocellata*
thiophanic acid	xanthone	orange	*Lecanora expallens*
strepsilin	dibenzofurane	green	*Cladonia strepsilis*
usnic acid	dibenzofurane: usnic acid	yellow*	*Cladonia portentosa*
arthoniaic acid	didepside	red	*Arthonia pruinata*
cryptochlorophaeic acid	didepside	pink*	*Cladonia chlorophaea* (race)
diploschistesic acid	didepside	red	*Diploschistes muscorum*
erythrin	didepside	carmine red	*Dirina massiliensis*
lecanoric acid	didepside	carmine red	*Lecanactis abietina, Melanelixia fuliginosa*
2'-O-methylanziaic acid	didepside	red	*Lecidea diducens*
2'-O-methylnorbarbatic acid	didepside	red	*Pseudocyphellaria norvegica*
2'-O-methylnorobtusatic acid	didepside	red	*Pseudocyphellaria norvegica*
nordivaricatic acid	didepside	pink*	*Lepraria crassissima*
olivetoric acid	didepside	red	*Pseudevernia furfuracea* var. *ceratea*
anziaic acid	didepside	carmine red	*Anzia japonica, Cetrelia sanguinea* (both E. Asia)
gyrophoric acid	tridepside	pink	*Ochrolechia androgyna, Hypotrachyna revoluta*
alectorialic acid	benzyldepside	pink*	*Alectoria nigricans, Fuscidea praeruptorum*
miriquidic acid	didepside	pink*	*Miriquidica leucophaea*

* a stronger and more easily observed reaction is obtained by pretreatment with K (the KC test).

TABLE 4. Examples of lichen substances causing coloured reactions with KC.

substance	chemical class	reaction	examples
α-alectoronic acid	depsidone	pink-red	*Cetrelia olivetorum* (race), *Arctoparmelia incurva*
physodic acid	depsidone	orange-pink	*Hypogymnia tubulosa, Pseudevernia furfuracea* var. *furfuracea*
lobaric acid	depsidone	violet	*Stereocaulon evolutum*
picrolichenic acid	depsone	violet-purple	*Pertusaria amara*

TABLE 5. Examples of substances causing coloured reactions with PD.			
substance	chemical class	reaction	examples
atranorin	didepside	yellow	*Punctelia subrudecta*
baeomycesic acid	didepside	orange	*Baeomyces roseus*
thamnolic acid	didepside	yellow-orange	*Cladonia parasitica, Ophioparma ventosa*
alectorialic acid	benzyldepside	bright yellow	*Buellia pulverea, Fuscidea praeruptorum*
fumarprotocetraric acid	depsidone	rust-red	*Cladonia pyxidata, C. ciliata*
argopsin	depsidone	red	*Halecania viridescens, Micarea leprosula, Phyllopsora rosei*
pannarin	depsidone	orange-red	*Pannaria rubiginosa*
physodalic acid	depsidone	orange	*Hypogymnia physodes*
protocetraric acid	depsidone	orange-red	*Flavoparmelia caperata*
psoromic acid	depsidone	bright yellow	*Schismatomma niveum, Squamarina cartilaginea* (chemotype)
salazinic acid	depsidone	orange	*Parmotrema reticulatum, Parmelia sulcata*

3. PIGMENTS
3.1. General
Pigments occur in most lichen species, and are important in classification at several taxonomic levels. Some pigments are found mainly in the thallus cortex, where they apparently function as filters of excessive light levels and harmful UV radiation.

Some lichen pigments are soluble in acetone and similar solvents, and can be extracted and studied by spot tests and thin-layer chromatography. The chemical structure of these soluble pigments is well-known, and they are typically light or vivid in colour, giving yellow, orange or red colours to lichen tissues. In contrast there is a range of pigments which are insoluble in acetone; these pigments are responsible for most of the brownish or blackish colours seen in lichen thalli and ascomata, although in thin section under the microscope they may also show yellow, orange, red, green or violet tints. Their chemical structure is unknown, and they are currently characterized by the colour changes which they may show with acids and alkalis.

The main classes of lichen pigments are shown in Table 6. Lichen tissues which are bright yellow or orange are likely to contain either quinones or pulvinic acid derivatives. These two classes can be distinguished by their reaction with K.

Quinones show a strongly coloured reaction with K, typically red or purple, but pulvinic acid derivatives are K − . Quinone pigments are yellow (rarely yellow-brown), orange or red; they are widespread in lichens, and also occur in non-lichenized fungi and in vascular plants. Examples of lichen quinones are listed in Table 7. The yellow and orange colour of the thallus in *Xanthoria* and many species of *Caloplaca* is due to anthraquinones, principally parietin. They are also responsible for the yellow or orange colour of the medulla in specimens of *Nephroma laevigatum, Phaeophyscia orbicularis* and *Solorina crocea*. Quinone pigments are responsible for the bright orange or red colour of certain apothecia, for instance rhodocladonic acid in *Cladonia floerkeana* and related species, haemoventosin in *Ophioparma ventosa* (both naphthaquinones), and anthraquinones in *Protoblastenia rupestris*. At least three different quinones are found in apothecia of the genus *Haematomma*. Quinone pigments are often soluble in cold acetone and can be studied by thin-layer chromatography (TLC), but some are almost insoluble or do not run on the TLC plate. Under the microscope, most quinone pigments found in lichens give a coloured solution with K, which helps to distinguish them from some pigments of unknown structure which are K + purple but which do not go into solution.

Pulvinic acid derivatives comprise a small group of pigments which are responsible for some yellow-green or bright yellow lichen thalli such as *Candelariella* spp. (calycin), *Chaenotheca chrysophthalma* (vulpinic acid) and *Rhizocarpon geographicum* (rhizocarpic acid). They do not react with K.

Lichen thalli which are pale yellow or yellowish-green often contain either xanthones or usnic acid. Xanthones are often C or KC + persistent yellow or orange. Usnic acid gives a KC + yellow reaction when a lichen extract is tested on filter paper, but other chemicals are often present which may give similar reactions or mask the reaction.

The green colour observed in some lichens (e.g. *Acarospora smaragdula*) when growing in copper-rich environments is apparently due to the formation of a copper-lichen acid complex; in the case of *A. smaragdula* this is copper-norstictic acid. This complex cannot be extracted by acetone, but the crystalline nature of the pigment can be established by polarized light, and the complex is broken down by K, to give the K + red (crystals) reaction typical of norstictic acid (Purvis *et al.* 1987).

3.2. Insoluble pigments of unknown structure

The chemical structure of these pigments is unknown, and they cannot be studied by TLC or other standard methods used in lichenology. Nevertheless, such pigments are of great importance in differentiating taxa, mainly at species level, and particularly in lecideoid lichens. Many authors have used informal names to describe the pigments that they have observed. Meyer & Printzen (2000) proposed a standard nomenclature for pigments found in lecideoid lichens, and introduced a method for typifying the named pigments by reference to a single collection of a standard species. Pigments are defined according to their colour in water, and their reactions with strong acids and bases. Colour reactions are often reversible and pH-dependent, but irreversible changes also occur, especially with strong acids.

3.2.1. Reagents
1. 10% potassium hydroxide solution (K; see section 2.1).
Meyer & Printzen (2000) recommended a 10-20% solution.

2. 10% hydrochloric acid (HCl).
A mixture of concentrated hydrochloric acid (i.e. 37% hydrochloric acid, density 1.19) and water 1: 9.
Meyer & Printzen recommended 10-20% hydrochloric acid.

3. 50% nitric acid (N).
A mixture of concentrated nitric acid (i.e. 63% nitric acid, density 1.42) and distilled water 1: 1.

4. Sodium hypochlorite solution (C; see section 2.1).
Undiluted household bleach. Used occasionally.

3.2.2. Procedure (based on Meyer & Printzen 2000)
The following procedure tests pH-dependent colour reactions with and without pretreatment with nitric acid. Reactions should be studied under a high-power microscope equipped with a light source of about 5000-6000° K, or with a blue filter placed in the path of the light. Reagents should be added

18

to the side of the coverslip and drawn into the preparation using tissue paper. Subtle colour changes are best appreciated by observing the reagent front as it passes across the section, but great care must be taken not to damage the microscope objective with the reagents. When a second reagent is applied, it is important that the section is completely infiltrated by the new reagent. If in doubt, parts of the following procedure can be repeated, transferring the section from one reagent to a fresh preparation in the next reagent, thus ensuring that the section is in equilibrium with the correct reagent.

CAUTION: nitric acid and potassium hydroxide must not come into contact with microscope lenses, and preparations should not be left on the microscope stage for longer than necessary.

1. Mount thin sections of ascoma in water on two separate slides, A and B.
2. Note colour of pigment in water.
3. Slide A:
      a. add K and note colour
      b. replace K by HCl and note colour
      c. replace HCl by further application of K and note colour
4. Slide B:
      a. add N and note colour
      b. replace by K and note colour
      c. replace by HCl and note colour
      d. replace by K and note colour

As an additional test to characterise some pigments, sections can be mounted in water, and C drawn under the coverslip. Sections which have been mounted in K or HCl can be studied at a neutral pH by washing them in one or in two successive drops of pH 7 buffer, although this is not necessary for routine testing. Note that the pigment colour in buffer is not necessarily the same as the colour in the intact and untreated lichen.

In addition to causing colour changes, K may cause other changes which should be carefully noted. Most insoluble pigments which change colour in K do so without dissolving; when pigment diffuses from the tissue in K, this should be noted. K often results in an intensification of a particular colour, without a change in hue; this is likely to be due in part to the clearing effect of K.

3.2.3. Interpretation of results

Care should be taken not to confuse colour changes of pigments with reactions of the reagents to other (colourless) lichen substances. In the hymenium of *Micarea prasina*, there is a pigment which produces a C + violet reaction; this may mask the fleeting C + orange-red reaction throughout the apothecium, which is due to the presence of gyrophoric acid. In this case the C + violet reaction is mostly confined to the upper part of the hymenium, whereas the C + red occurs in all parts of the hymenium.

There are a number of difficulties associated with the study of insoluble pigments:
1. The perceived colour of the pigment is dependent upon the concentration of the pigment, so that one pigment may appear as, for instance, yellow to brown in the same section.
2. Different workers are likely to describe the same colour changes in slightly different colour terms.
3. More than one pigment may occur in the same apothecium or same tissue, and some overlapping of pigments may occur.

For these reasons, the pigments of a particular taxon should be carefully compared with those of the control species before they are identified.

3.2.4. Identification of acetone-insoluble pigments

The pigments described by Meyer & Printzen (2000) and later authors are listed in Table 8. The original colour terms are largely followed for the sake of uniformity, but some observations by the present authors have been added. Where these appear to differ from the observations of Meyer & Printzen, it may be due in part merely to differences in the use of colour terms.

Notes on the pigments:

Each pigment is defined by reference to a standard taxon, which is listed below. Other examples are given when possible.

Arceutina-yellow: based on *Bacidia arceutina* (epihymenium and hypothecium). Other examples: *Bacidia rubella* (dilute). The pigment appears yellowish when dilute, but appears as brown where it is dense. It shows only subtle changes with altered pH, dulling in HCl and brightening in K.

Arnoldiana-brown: based on *Bacidia arnoldiana* (hypothecium and exciple). A slightly reddish brown which dulls in K and is brighter in HCl.

Atra-brown: based on *Opegrapha atra* (exciple). The pigment in water appears to the present authors as dark reddish brown; it has a dull greenish tint in K. We also found that pretreatment with N changes the reactions, and that in K after N there are scarcely any greenish tints.

Atra-red: based on *Tephromela atra* (hymenium). Other examples: *Farnoldia jurana, Immersaria athroocarpa, Rhizocarpon lecanorinum, R. viridiatrum.* There appear to be distinct purplish or even violet tints in K. N weakens subsequent reactions.

Bagliettoana-green: based on *Bacidia bagliettoana* (epihymenium). Other examples: epihymenia of *B. egenula, B. subincompta.*

Caesiocinerea-green: based on *Aspicilia caesiocinerea* (epihymenium). Other examples: *Trapeliopsis flexuosa* (epihymenium). A pigment which is distinctly green in HCl, but brownish in K; reactions not affected by N.

Cinereorufa-green: based on *Schaereria cinereorufa* (epihymenium). Other examples: *S. fuscocinerea.* In some specimens, the reactions are obscured by large quantities of Hypnorum-blue.

Elachista-brown: based on *Micarea elachista* (epihymenium). The colour change between water and K is small.

Hertelii-green: based on *Biatora hertelii* (Madeira; subhymenium). Other examples: *Biatora britannica.*

Hypnorum-blue: based on *Lecidea hypnorum* (granules in hymenium). Other examples: *Schaereria cinereorufa, S. fuscocinerea.* This pigment is violet (not blue) both in water and when transferred to pH 7 buffer after K and HCl treatment, although the small granules of *L. hypnorum* may appear blackish in water, and the colour is hard to discern.

Intrusa-yellow: based on *Scoliciosporum intrusum* (cytoplasm of some ascogenous hyphae, asci and ascospores).

Laurocerasi-brown: based on *Bacidia laurocerasi* (epihymenium, sometimes with Arceutina-yellow). Other examples: *B. biatorina.* The sequence water/K/HCl/K typically results in a dull greenish grey (not purplish) colour, going into solution. In low concentrations the pigment may appear greyish brown in water.

Leptocline-brown: based on *Buellia leptocline*. Other examples: *B. saxorum*, *B. subdisciformis*. An important feature is the reddish brown colour in water, giving a coloured solution in K. The pigment is precipitated from solution by HCl and redissolved by additional K (this is a common feature of many pigments).

Leptoclinoides-brown: based on *Buellia leptoclinoides*.

Macrocarpa-green: based on *Porpidia macrocarpa* (epihymenium). Other examples: *Rhizocarpon hochstetteri*, *R. infernulum*. Duller in colour than Cinereorufa-green (Fryday 2002).

Melaena-red: based on *Micarea melaena* (hypothecium). Observations are complicated by the frequent presence of three pigments in the apothecium of *M. melaena*: Cinereorufa-green (hymenium), Melaena-red (typically in outer part of hypothecium) and Melaenida-red (often dominating the hypothecium).

Melaenida-red: based on *Micarea melaenida* (hypothecium). Other examples: *M. melaena* (hypothecium, with Melaena-red).

Pausiaca-green: based on *Biatora pausiaca* (epihymenium) (Printzen & Tønsberg 2003).

Peregrina-blue: based on *Buellia peregrina* (Bungartz & Wirth 2007).

Polychroa-brown: based on *Bacidia polychroa* (hypothecium and epihymenium, occurring with Arceutina-yellow).

Pontica-blue: based on *Biatora pontica* (hypothecium, in part) (Printzen & Tønsberg 2003).

Pontica-red: based on *Biatora pontica* (hypothecium, in part) (Printzen & Tønsberg 2003).

Porina-yellow: based on *Porina nucula*, *P. epiphylla*, *P. lectissima* and others (involucrellum) (Hafellner & Kalb 1995).

Sagedia-red: based on *Porina mammillosa*, *P. linearis* and others (involucrellum) (Hafellner & Kalb 1995).

Schweinitzii-red: based on *Bacidia schweinitzii* (N. America; hymenium and exciple).

Sedifolia-grey: based on *Toninia sedifolia* (epihymenium). Other examples: *Caloplaca alociza*, *C. chalybaea*, *Micarea globulosella*, *M. prasina*. The present authors found that the pigment was dull violaceous in HCl, and not greenish grey. The sequence water/K/HCl/K produces a strong violet reaction, much stronger than K alone. The pigment is also C + violet.

Superba-brown: based on *Porpidia superba* (hypothecium and parts of exciple). Other examples: *Clauzadea monticola* (hypothecium). A reddish to orangey brown pigment which dulls in K and brightens in HCl. Reactions are not affected by pretreatment with N. After K/HCl/K treatment, there is a trace of brown solution, which forms a precipitate on addition of more HCl.

Verrucarioides-brown: based on *Toninia verrucarioides* (epihymenium). Observations are complicated by the possible occurrence of traces of a greenish, HCl + violet pigment, and by occasional traces of hypothecial pigment in the epihymenium.

TABLE 6. The main classes of pigments found in lichens.

colour	reaction with K and KC	solubility in cold acetone	example species	chemical class
bright yellow or yellow-green (intact thallus)	K − (or fading)	soluble	*Candelariella* spp., *Chaenotheca furfuracea, C. hispidula, Chrysothrix* spp., *Lecanora epanora, Psilolechia lucida, Rhizocarpon geographicum*	pulvinic acid derivatives
pale yellow (intact thallus pale yellow to yellowish-green)	K −, KC + yellow	soluble	*Cladonia ciliata* var. *tenuis, C. diversa, C. portentosa, Evernia prunastri, Lecanora sulphurea, Flavoparmelia caperata*	usnic acid
pale yellow (intact thallus often pale yellow to yellowish-green; extracts on filter paper or TLC plates yellow to almost colourless)	K − or yellowish, KC − or + yellow to orange	soluble	*Bacidia viridifarinosa, Buellia ocellata, Lecanora expallens* (also with usnic acid), *Lecidella elaeochroma, Pertusaria flavicans, P. flavida, Pyrrhospora quernea*	xanthones
yellow, orange or red (intact lichen, or microscopic)	K + purple, rarely blue, colour going into solution	soluble to almost insoluble	Thallus of *Caloplaca flavescens, Solorina crocea, Mycoblastus sanguinarius, Xanthoria parietina;* apothecia of *Arthonia elegans, A. cinnabarina, Cladonia floerkeana, Opegrapha ochrocheila, Ophioparma ventosa, Piccolia ochrophora, Protoblastenia rupestris*	quinones
often brown or black in intact lichen, but variously brown, orange, red, violet, or green in thin section under the microscope	various	insoluble	Thallus of *Melanelixia fuliginosa, Verrucaria nigrescens;* pigments in ascomata of most species.	structure unknown ('acetone-insoluble pigments')

22

TABLE 7. Examples of quinone and quinone-like pigments in lichens.

name	colour	reaction with K	solubility in cold acetone	examples	notes
canarione	yellow	black; at lower concentrations of K, red to deep purple, going into solution	good	*Lethariella canariensis* (thallus)	naphthaquinone
haemoventosin	red (intact apothecia); orange under microscope	deep blue, then violet, going into solution (microscope)	good	*Ophioparma ventosa* (apothecia)	naphthaquinone
rhodocladonic acid	orange-red (under microscope)	red (going into solution)	poor	*Cladonia floerkeana, C. macilenta* (apothecia), *C. norvegica* (thallus where attacked by mites), *Mycoblastus sanguinarius* (thallus)	naphthaquinone; the red pigment in all red-fruited *Cladonia* species.
7-7'-bis(1,4,5,8-tetrahydroxy-3-ethylnaphtha-2,6-quinone) (tentative)	purplish red	purplish violet, going into solution	good	*Flavocetraria cucullata* (predominant pigment in base of thallus, occurs with other quinones)	bis-naphthaquinone
bellidiflorin	yellow (extracts)	yellow-brown, going into solution	good	*Cladonia bellidiflora, C. polydactyla* (podetia, especially base)	anthraquinone (probably an iron complex); with c. 2 other pigments in TLC of *Cladonia*.
7-chloroemodin	orange-brown (under microscope, in *Pyrrhospora*)	purplish red, going into solution	good	Apothecia of *Pyrrhospora quernea*, exciple of *Adelolechia pilati*, thallus of *Heterodermia obscurata* (major), *Lasallia papulosa, Nephroma laevigatum* (major).	anthraquinone
emodin	orange (pure sample, under microscope)	purplish red, going into solution	good	Thallus of *Nephroma laevigatum* (major or trace)	anthraquinone; commercially available (Sigma-Aldrich)

23

TABLE 7 (continued). Examples of quinone and quinone-like pigments in lichens.

russulone	orange (under microscope)	purple-red, going into solution, soon forming precipitate	rather poor	*Haematomma ochroleucum, H. nemetzii* (Mediterranean), *H. persoonii* (mainly pantropical); apothecia	anthraquinone.
haematommone	orange-red (under microscope)	violet, going into solution, then fading, with no precipitate	rather poor	*Haematomma flexuosum* (tropics and subtropics), *H. sorediatum* (W. Europe, Madeira, America, India, Australia); apothecia	anthraquinone
parietin	yellow (whole thallus, and under microscope)	red-purple, going into solution	good	*Xanthoria parietina*	anthraquinone (the major pigment in most yellow *Caloplaca* and *Xanthoria* species)
solorinic acid	orange (intact thallus, and extract)	red-purple, going into solution	good	*Solorina crocea* (medulla)	anthraquinone
skyrin	yellow to orange (in thallus)	red-purple, going into solution	rather poor	*Phaeophyscia orbicularis* (some), *P. endococcina, P. endophoenicea* (thallus of all)	bis-anthraquinone
polyporic acid	yellow-brown (pure sample, under microscope)	dissolving to give violet solution, soon recrystallizing as the violet potassium salt	very poor	*Pseudocyphellaria colensoi* (thallus), *Hapalopilus nidulans* (non-lichenized basidiomycete; abundant in fruit body)	terphenylquinone
unknown	orange (under microscope)	red-purple, going into solution	very poor	*Pyrenula nitida* (perithecium)	
unknown	yellow to purple-red (whole thallus and under microscope)	violet (not going into solution)	very poor	*Thelidium fontigenum* (thallus)	quinone-like pigment; colour is pH-dependent, yellow at pH 7.

24

TABLE 8. Colour reactions of some named ascomatal pigments.
Adapted from Meyer & Printzen (2000). For procedure, see text. Pigments listed in order of colour in water: blue, brown, green, grey, red and yellow.

Pigment	water	K		HCl	N	K		HCl
Hypnorum-blue	violet or violaceous black (granular)	turquoise	↔	violet	negative (violet)	turquoise	↔	violet
Pontica-blue	dark blue, turquoise	purple	↔	violaceous, becoming brighter red in K on repetition	negative	bright purple-red violaceous	↔	dark
Peregrina-blue	blue	green changing to brown	↔	reddish	wine-red		↔	
Arnoldiana-brown	reddish brown	dark brown (dull greyish brown)	↔	reddish brown (orangey brown)	negative (reddish brown or orangey brown)	dark brown (dull greyish brown)	↔	reddish brown (orangey brown)
Atra-brown	matt brown (dark reddish brown)	olive-black (dull grey-green or greenish grey-brown)	↔	matt brown (reddish brown)	reddish brown	olive-black (dull grey brown with at most a slight greenish tone)	↔	reddish brown
Elachista-brown	fuscous brown	yellowish brown (going into solution)	↔	sordid olive brown (slightly dulling from K)	negative	yellowish brown (going into solution)	↔	sordid olive brown

25

TABLE 8 (continued). Colour reactions of some ascomatal pigments. Adapted from Meyer & Printzen (2000). For procedure, see text.

Pigment	water	K		HCl	N	K		HCl
Laurocerasi-brown	reddish or purplish brown (dark purplish brown)	dark purple (to greyish violaceous brown)	↔	pinkish brown (dark purplish brown)	pinkish to reddish brown (red with purplish tint)	sordid grey-green (dull greyish or greenish brown)	↔	pinkish to reddish brown (red with purplish tint)
Leptocline-brown	dark red brown	orange brown (yellow to reddish brown solution)	↔	intensely red brown (yellow brown to brown)	negative	clear yellowish brown	↔	dull yellowish brown
Leptoclinoides-brown	brown	dull brown	↔	yellowish brown	orange-brown	dull brown	↔	orange intensifying
Polychroa-brown	orange-brown to ochre	red to violaceous	↔	yellow-orange	yellow-orange	dark yellow to orange-brown	↔	pale yellow
Ruginosa-brown	dark red (dark red-brown with slight purplish tinge)	red intensifying (purple)	↔	brownish red (dark red brown)	brownish red (dark red brown intensifying)	brown (dissolving) (purple with a red-brown solution)	↔	brown (red brown)
Superba-brown	orange-brown to ochre (reddish-brown, to orangey brown where dilute)	dull brown	↔	orange intensifying (red-brown to dark orange-brown)	orange intensifying	dull brown	↔	orange intensifying (red-brown to orangey brown)

TABLE 8 (continued). Colour reactions of some ascomatal pigments. Adapted from Meyer & Printzen (2000). For procedure, see text

Pigment	water	K		HCl	N	K		HCl
Verrucarioides-brown	dull brown	violaceous brown	↔	dull brown	darker brown or negative (or dull red ?)	violaceous brown	↔	dark brown (or dull red)
Pausiaca-green	olivaceous brown	brown	↔	pale olivaceous	dull brown	brownish orange	↔	dull olivaceous
Bagliettoana-green	pale to brownish green (dull green to dull bluish green)	green (dull green or dull bluish green, almost negative)	↔	violaceous (distinct violet)	violaceous ± blue crystals (distinct violet)	pale to brownish green (dull green to dull bluish green)	↔	violaceous (violet)
Caesiocinerea-green	olive, sordid green	yellowish brown (dull brown, not or scarcely greenish)	↔	green (dark green)	green intensifying (dark green)	yellowish brown (dull brown, not or scarcely greenish)	↔	green (dark green)
Cinereorufa-green	(dark) green, turquoise (bluish green)	green	↔	blue, blue-green	violaceous, red to red-brown, purplish	green	↔	violaceous (red-purple)
Macrocarpa-green	dull olivaceous green	unchanged	↔		reddish brown	grey-green	↔	reddish brown

27

TABLE 8 (continued). Colour reactions of some ascomatal pigments. Adapted from Meyer & Printzen (2000). For procedure, see text

Pigment	water		K		HCl		N	K		HCl
Hertelii-green	(dark green), turquoise	↔	green	↔	violaceous	↔	orange to purplish	orange	↔	pale yellow
Sedifolia-grey	blackish grey, grey-green (dark brownish grey)	↔	pink to violaceous (dark violaceous brown)	↔	greenish grey (dull violaceous brown)	↔	violaceous grey	pinkish brown to violaceous (strong violet)	↔	greenish grey or turquoise (dull violaceous)
Atra-red	dark red (dark red-purple)	↔	red (purple to purple-violet)	↔	brownish red (dull purplish brown)	↔	orange red (dark red)	brownish (reddish purplish brown or dull faded violet)	↔	light orange-red (reddish purple-brown)
Melaena-red	purple	↔	green	↔	purple	↔	red intensifying	sordid olive - vanishing		
Sagedia-red	purple-violet to purple	↔	dark bluish grey	↔	purple to red-purple	↔			↔	
Melaenida-red	purple (purplish brown)	↔	red intensifying (dark purplish brown)	↔	pale purple (purple brown to reddish brown)	↔	negative (dark red to purplish red)	red intensifying (dark purplish brown to reddish brown)	↔	pale purple (dull purplish red or brown)

28

TABLE 8 (continued). Colour reactions of some ascomatal pigments. Adapted from Meyer & Printzen (2000). For procedure, see text.

Pigment	water	K		HCl	N	K		HCl
Pontica-red	dark red or purple	bright purple-red	↔	dark violaceous	negative or violaceous	bright purple-red	↔	dark violaceous
Schweinitzii-red	dark red	no change	↔	no change	red intensifying or negative	no change	↔	no change
Arceutina-yellow	pale yellow (yellowish brown, yellow when dilute)	orange-yellow (slightly intensifying)	↔	pale yellow (dull yellowish brown)	negative (dull brown)	orange-yellow (yellowish brown)	↔	pale yellow (dull yellowish brown)
Porina-yellow	yellow to orange	orange or dark orange	↔	yellow to orange			↔	
Intrusa-yellow	yellow	purple	↔	yellow	negative	purple	↔	yellow

4. IODINE REACTIONS

Iodine forms coloured complexes with some of the classes of polysaccharides (rarely other lichen substances) which are found in hyphal walls and in extracellular gels; these reactions are valuable at various taxonomic levels. The simple presence or absence of I + reactions in the medulla is routinely used as a character to discriminate taxa, for instance in identification of species in genera such as *Buellia*, *Porpidia*, and *Rhizocarpon*. The more specific identification of polysaccharides such as lichenan has taxonomic significance at the generic level in *Parmeliaceae*. The reactions of the hymenium and particularly of the ascus apex are of major importance in modern lichen taxonomy at the level of genus and above.

Positive reactions with iodine reagents are usually bluish or reddish; yellow or amber staining caused by simple absorption of iodine is a negative reaction. Reactions with iodine reagents vary according to factors such as composition of the reagent, the concentration of the reagent, and whether the sample has been pre-treated with KOH. Different workers have used a variety of formulae, which give different staining reactions in certain conditions, and there is still no generally agreed standard for routine testing. Iodine is volatile, and prepared solutions gradually lose iodine. In critical work using iodine reactions it is necessary to use freshly prepared solutions and to carefully specify the conditions of use.

Much of the following is based on the thorough treatment of I + substances by Common (1991).

4.1. Reagents

Widely used reagents for routine use:

1. Lugol's solution (Hawksworth *et al.* 1995)

iodine	0.5 g
potassium iodide	1.5 g
distilled water	100 ml

An iodine solution for general use. Widely differing formulations of 'Lugol's solution' have been used by different workers; the precise formulation may not be of critical importance for routine use in detecting I + bluish thalline reactions, and observing details of the ascus tip. Baral (1987) recommended an iodine solution for general use which comprised 1 g iodine, 3 g potassium iodide, and 100 g water

2. Lugol's solution in lactic acid
As Lugol's solution, but the water is replaced by lactic acid.
Gives stronger reactions than normal Lugol's solution in some instances.

3. Melzer's Reagent (Melzer 1924)

iodine	1.0 g
potassium iodide	3.0 g
chloral hydrate	40.0 g
distilled water	40.0 ml

The final volume is approx. 63 ml; iodine concentration is approx. 1.6% w/v.

This is the original formula, also used by Baral (1987) and Common (1991). Other formulations have been used by different workers. The main advantage of Melzer's reagent in certain situations is the clearing effect on tissues. It has been used relatively little by lichenologists, but it has been used to stain the I + purple ascospores of *Graphis* and related genera, and it is the most convenient reagent for demonstrating the I + medulla of *Dermatocarpon luridum* in routine identification work.

4. Zinc-chlor-iodide (Gahan 1984)
zinc chloride	30g
potassium iodide	5g
iodine	1 g
distilled water	14 ml

Formulations of zinc-chlor-iodide are used to detect cellulose (see below).

Additional reagents for critical work:

5. Iodine-potassium iodide (IKI) solutions (Common 1991)
These are expressed as percentage of iodine on weight/volume basis; the weight of KI is twice that of the iodine in each case.

Stock solution (20% IKI):
iodine	20 g
potassium iodide	40 g
distilled water to make volume up to 100 ml.	

Dissolve iodine and KI in small volume of water at first, then make up to final volume (iodine dissolves better in stronger solutions of KI).

Prepare other concentrations of IKI by dilution of the stock solution. In addition to 20% IKI, Common (1991) found the following dilutions to be most useful:
1.5% IKI: make up 7.5 ml of 20% IKI to 100 ml with distilled water.
0.15% IKI: make up 10 ml of 1.5% IKI to 100 ml with distilled water.
Iodine is volatile, and the weaker dilutions should be changed every few days.

6. Calcium chloride-iodine-potassium iodide (CaIKI) solution (Common 1991)

Stock solution of calcium chloride:
calcium chloride (anhydrous)	44.4 g
distilled water to make up to 100 ml total volume.	

Make working solution by combining $CaCl_2$ stock solution with 1.5% IKI in the proportion of 9: 1.

7. Lactophenol-iodine-potassium iodide solutions (LPIKI) (Common 1991)

lactophenol stock solution:
lactic acid	60 g (50 ml)
glycerol	120 g (99 ml)
phenol	60 g

For 0.15% LPIKI: mix stock lactophenol solution and 20% IKI in proportion 1: 133.
For 0.4% LPIKI: mix lactophenol stock solution and 20% IKI in proportion 1: 50.

8. Sulphuric acid-IKI solution (SIKI) (Common 1991)
dissolve 0.45 g iodine and 3.0 g KI in water to make 15 ml solution; combine with 15 ml of 10% H_2SO_4 (i.e. 15 ml of a mixture of concentrated sulphuric acid [i.e. 98% sulphuric acid, density 1.84] and distilled water in the proportion 1: 9).

9. Zinc chloride-iodine-potassium iodide (ZnIKI) (Common 1991)

Stock solution of zinc chloride:
zinc chloride	100 g
potassium iodide	35 g
distilled water	60 ml.

Combine with 1.5% IKI in proportion 9: 1.

This reagent is similar but not identical to zinc-chlor-iodide.

4.2. Non-specific I + reactions for routine identification

Routine tests for I + bluish substances in the thallus are often used to discriminate taxa at species level. The nature of the substance involved is often not stated, although it is often assumed to be isolichenan. Although many species possess substances with similar staining reactions to isolichenan from *Cetraria islandica* (from which it was first isolated), they may prove to be different when proper chemical analyses are carried out.

Procedure:
Place a thin section directly into Lugol's solution, 1.5% IKI, or Melzer's reagent. Alternatively, mount the tissue, or make a thin squash of tissue, in water and draw the iodine reagent under the coverslip with tissue paper. Medullary tissues of many lichen species produce lavender, violet or bluish reactions with iodine reagents, but weak reactions often appear greyish.

I + bluish reactions with iodine reagents are often made stronger by pre-treatment with K. The section can be immersed in a small drop of K and transferred directly to a drop of iodine reagent. For crustose material it is highly recommended that sections are pretreated with K and then tested with Lugol's solution in lactic acid. Following treatment with K, an I + bluish substance is often seen in suspension outside the thallus section when it is added to Lugol's solution, especially in lactic acid. A similar phenomenon can be demonstrated in *Cetraria islandica*, and may be caused by the known mobility of isolichenan in K.

It is generally recommended that iodine reactions are observed at a magnification of × 100 or more using a microscope. However, strong reactions are often easily seen under the dissecting microscope, and in a few instances reactions may be seen more easily with the dissecting microscope than with high power. For instance, the upper surface of dry sections of the medulla of *Sphaerophorus globosus* may turn a distinct blue colour when placed on a small drop of Lugol's solution and observed under the dissecting microscope, but the colour is dull greyish once the section is saturated, and appears pale greyish under high power. Material which is difficult to section, such as certain crustose species, may sometimes be easier to test under the dissecting microscope, but attempts should be made to view material under high power unless a clear reaction can be seen.

Examples of species with an I + bluish reaction in the medulla are *Lecidea lactea*, *Porpidia speirea*, *P. tuberculosa*, and *Sphaerophorus globosus*.

4.3. Methods for identification and localization of specific types of polysaccharide

Common (1991) applied a series of tests involving iodine reactions to characterize I + polysaccharides in lichens. Although Common's work was directed particularly towards *Parmeliaceae*, the tests may be used to describe and compare I + materials in any group of lichens. It should be stressed that more than one type of I + polysaccharide may occur together in the same species, also that not all I + polysaccharides are well-characterized and understood. For these reasons, interpretation of the results of iodine tests, in terms of specific groups of polysaccharides, must be made with caution.

General procedure:
The procedure can be carried out on a microscope slide.

Prepare thin sections of the thallus.
Wet sections in 95% alcohol.
Place sections in commercial sodium hypochlorite bleach (C) just long enough to decolourize them.
Rinse thoroughly in water.
Place section in large drop of iodine reagent on slide and agitate with needle for 30s.
Draw off reagent, replace with fresh drop, and add coverslip.
Observe preparation with microscope aperture diaphragm wide open.

Sections may be tested in any of the iodine reagents listed above. With few exceptions, a new section should be used for each of the reagents.

Additional tests:
The 20%→0.15% IKI test:
Place bleached sections in 20% IKI for about one minute.
Rinse in 1.5% IKI.
Place in 0.15% IKI and agitate until equilibrium reached.
Observe as above.

Precipitation tests for lichenan: the h-1.5% IKI and h-SIKI tests (Common 1991).
Place material (section or small fragment) on slide in large drop of SIKI or 1.5% IKI and agitate as usual.
Apply coverslip; place on hotplate adjusted to slightly over boiling point.
When temperature is correctly adjusted, solution will begin to boil gently in about 20-30 s.
After 2-3 s boiling, remove from hotplate (violent or prolonged boiling must be avoided).
Allow to cool for several minutes, then observe.

A coloured precipitate surrounding the tissue is a positive reaction. In these tests, some other substances can also form precipitates: stictic acid may do so, but this forms radial clusters of fine crystals. Fatty acids form yellow oily droplets with the h-SIKI test.

4.4. The iodine reactions of specific groups of polysaccharides
The reactions of major groups of I + polysaccharides in lichens are summarized in Table 9. Note that not all I + reactions in lichens have been attributed to a particular group of polysaccharides, and therefore some are not included in the table.

1. Lichenan
Two types of lichenan, the *Cetraria*-type, and the *Xanthoparmelia*-type, together with some intermediate types, were found by Common (1991). Lichenan-like reactions are taxonomically important in the family *Parmeliaceae*, mainly at a genus or subfamily level. Within a specimen lichenan is almost always either abundant and easily detected, or completely undetectable (Common 1991). Common did not find lichenan reactions outside the family *Parmeliaceae*. A summary of lichenan distribution in *Parmeliaceae* was given in Elix (1993). Lichenan distribution in selected genera is shown in Table 10.

Cetraria-type lichenan:
The reactions of this substance include: 0.15% IKI − , 1.5% IKI + reddish, CaIKI + intense red, 20%→0.15% IKI test negative (colourless). In the h-1.5% IKI test, it forms a cloud of purplish-red granules around the specimen, and forms a cloud of coarser, red granules in the h-SIKI test.
Examples: *Cetraria islandica, Platismatia glauca*.

Xanthoparmelia-type lichenan:
The reactions of this substance are similar to those of the *Cetraria*-type above, but in the h-1.5% IKI test there is only a trace of a red precipitate, and the 20%→0.15% IKI test results in a blue colouration.
Examples: *Xanthoparmelia conspersa, X. loxodes*

The two main types of lichenan are best distinguished by the 20%→0.15% IKI test and the h-1.5% IKI test. The reaction with ZnIKI also differentiates the two, with the *Cetraria*-type negative, and the *Xanthoparmelia*-type purplish. True reddish reactions occur in some intermediate types, but some apparent red reactions are 'false positives'. To eliminate false positives, first run tissue through a series of zinc chloride solutions (25%, 50%, full strength) then place in ZnIKI.

2. Isolichenan
Isolichenan is typically confined to vegetative structures in lichens, with a few exceptions such as the hymenium of some species of *Graphidaceae*. Isolichenan is I + lilac to lavender in all iodine reagents, but reactions are often weak, and not equally visible in all reagents. Weak reactions often appear greyish, and can be obscured by the yellow (I −) colour of the background. There is a continuum from distinct to scarcely perceptible reactions, and when present in low quantities isolichenan may not be demonstrable using iodine reagents. When reactions are weak, the best procedure is as follows:

Wet and bleach sections.
Stain in 0.15% IKI
Transfer to 0.15% LPIKI and agitate. This reagent has a clearing effect which makes weak reactions more easily visible.
Observe under low magnification (× 10 objective).

Examples: *Cetraria islandica*: reactions in most reagents are obscured by the presence of lichenan in this species, but the 20%→0.15% IKI test gives a lavender reaction which is attributable to isolichenan alone. Isolichenan is recorded from many species of the *Parmeliaceae*, but is difficult to demonstrate.

3. Amylomycan
Iodine reactions in asci and associated gel, and in ascogenous hyphae (which are all dikaryotic tissues) are probably caused by a single family of polysaccharides with a wide but continuous spectrum of staining characteristics, termed amylomycan by Common (1991). Although typical amylomycan-type reactions are generally restricted to dikaryotic tissues, they can also be found in the thalli of most genera of Arthoniales, including *Opegrapha*. At one extreme are forms which are I + blue in all concentrations of iodine. At the other extreme are forms with are I − at very low concentration, but I + reddish at higher concentrations. Most lichens are intermediate between these extremes, and stain I + blue at low iodine concentrations and reddish at higher concentrations. The point at which the iodine concentration is sufficient to change the I + reaction from blue to red is called the critical point. Forms with a low critical point are I − in Melzer's reagent. Pre-treatment of the red or intermediate forms with KOH changes the staining properties so that they are blue at high I concentration, and I + blue with Melzer's reagent.

Baral (1987) distinguished two reactions within the amylomycan continuum under the following names; the hemiamyloid reaction is only I + blue at low concentrations of iodine or after pretreatment with KOH:

	< 1% I	≥ 1% I	≥ 1% I after pretreatment with KOH
hemiamyloid	I – or I + red or blue	I + red	I + blue
euamyloid	I + blue	I + blue	I + blue

The reactions of some forms of amylomycan are superficially similar to isolichenan reactions; some of the differences include:

a. heat stability: bring material on a slide to boiling point in LPIKI; remove and immediately view microscopically. The isolichenan-type reaction is more heat-stable and remains visible, but hymenial (amylomycan) reactions are lost, and only return when cooled somewhat;

b. isolichenan-type reactions are weakened by KOH pretreatment (apparently by extraction), whereas hymenial reactions become more strongly blue;

c. at least in the *Parmeliaeae*, isolichenan-type reactions are never as intense as hymenial reactions, and are more lilac or lavender in shade (rather than blue).

4. Cellulose

Cellulose occurs in the cell wall of photobionts. Formulations of zinc-chlor-iodide have been used to detect cellulose, for instance to demonstrate the presence of dead algal cells in the cortex of certain lichens (e.g. Timdal 1984). Common (1991) found that cell walls of *Trebouxia* stained reddish in Melzer's reagent, dark purplish in ZnIKI, and blue after the 20%→0.15% IKI.

5. Other polysaccharides

There are a number of I + reactions which have not been attributed to an identifiable group of polysaccharides. For instance, the I + red reaction of the gel within the thallus of species of *Collema* has been attributed to glycogen, but Baral (1987) considered this was unlikely to be correct. The minimum concentration of iodine necessary to give a reaction is said to vary greatly between the species (see Degelius 1954).

6. Non-polysaccharide lichen substances

A number of lichen substances can form bright red or blue complexes under certain conditions, most notably stictic acid (Common 1991).

4.5. Ascus structures

The iodine staining reactions of asci, and particularly the distribution of I + structures in the ascus apex, are important characters in lichen taxonomy. Staining is carried out with Lugol's solution. Investigation of the ascus apex, particularly the tholus of lecanoralean and lecideoid lichens, requires a little care and patience. Some workers have used a Lugol's solution in lactic acid instead of water. Each worker will probably evolve a personal working procedure, but general principles are:

♦ The asci should not be obscured by other asci or paraphyses: thin sections or small pieces of hymenial tissue should be used; some workers have cut out individual asci from sections using fine needles.

♦ The asci should not be damaged by cutting or excessive squashing.

♦ Immature asci should be observed: it may be necessary to observe large numbers of asci to find undamaged asci at a suitable stage of development.

♦ Pretreatment with KOH is often necessary, at least to speed up the staining reaction, and to soften the gel surrounding the asci. Some authors use 10% KOH, others claim that this can damage the ascus apex and weaker solutions should be used.

♦ The concentration of iodine reagent in the preparation may need to be adjusted to give the optimum amount of detail: if overstaining occurs, it can be reduced by carefully drawing very dilute KOH under the coverslip with tissue paper. In some cases the inner structures can be fleetingly observed as darkly staining outer structures are bleached first.

<u>General procedure:</u>
- Place a thin section of an ascoma onto a slide; remove any large pieces of non-hymenial tissue. The moistened hymenium can be removed intact from some pyrenocarps.
- Add a drop of 10% KOH and leave for 1-5 minutes (or longer if the hymenium has a dense gelatinous matrix).
- Remove most of the KOH with the edge of a tissue.
- Add a drop of Lugol's solution, carefully lower a coverslip on to the preparation without disturbing the tissue. Normal Lugol's solution stains many lecanoralean asci too darkly, and it should be diluted with water; some workers recommend a 0.3% Lugol's solution.
- Observe under high power of the microscope.
- If there is no bluing of the asci or hymenial gel, make another preparation, but soak up the first drop of Lugol's solution with tissue, and add another. This step may need to be repeated to ensure a sufficient iodine concentration (note that some taxa are always I - , which is a useful taxonomic character in itself).
- Tap coverslip gently, if neccesary, to spread the tissues.

TABLE 9. Summary of iodine reactions of some major groups of polysaccharides (adapted from Common 1991)

MATERIAL	KOH pretreatment	0.15% IKI	1.5% IKI	0.15% LPIKI	CaIKI	ZnIKI	Melzer's solution	20→0.15% IKI
isolichenan	no	bluish	bluish	bluish	bluish	bluish	bluish	bluish
	yes	bluish	bluish	bluish	bluish	bluish	bluish	bluish
lichenan: Cetraria-type	no	none	red	none	red	none	orange	none
	yes	none	red					
lichenan: Xanthoparmelia-type	no	none	red	none	red	bluish	red	blue
	yes	none	red					
amylomycan: extreme red form ('hemiamyloid' in part)	no	red	red	none	red	none	none	
	yes	blue	blue	blue	blue	blue	blue	
amylomycan: intermediate form ('hemiamyloid' in part)	no	blue or red	red	none or blue	red	none or blue	none or blue	
	yes	blue	blue	blue	blue	blue	blue	
amylomycan: extreme blue form ('euamyloid')	no	blue	blue	blue	blue	blue	blue	
	yes	blue	blue	blue	blue	blue	blue	

37

TABLE 10. Distribution of lichenan in selected genera of *Parmeliaceae*. Compiled from Common (1991) and Elix (1993).

	Cetraria-type	*Xanthoparmelia*-type	intermediate types	examples
Alectoria	+		± traces	*Alectoria ochroleuca, A. nigricans*
Bryoria	+			*Bryoria capillaris, B. fuscescens, B. subcana*
Cetraria	+			*Cetraria aculeata, C. islandica*
Cornicularia	+		+	*Cornicularia normoerica*
Imshaugia	+			*Imshaugia aleurites*
Platismatia	+			*Platismatia glauca*
Parmotrema			+	*Parmotrema reticulatum*
Xanthoparmelia		+		*Xanthoparmelia conspersa, X. delisei, X. mougeotii, X. pulla*
Cetrelia				*Cetrelia olivetorum*
Flavoparmelia				*Flavoparmelia caperata*
Hypotrachyna				*Hypotrachyna laevigata, H. revoluta*
Melanelixia				*Melanelixia fuliginosa, M. subaurifera*
Melanohalea				*M. elegantula, M. exasperata, M. laciniatula*
Parmelia				*Parmelia omphalodes, P. saxatilis, P. sulcata*
Parmelina				*Parmelina quercina, P. tiliacea, P. pastillifera*
Pleurosticta				*Pleurosticta acetabulum*
Punctelia				*Punctelia borreri, P. subrudecta*
Parmeliopsis				*Parmeliopsis ambigua P. hyperopta*

5. STAINS

Relatively few stains are used routinely in the study of lichens They are largely outside the scope of this book, as in most cases they do not allow identification of particular substances. However, Common & Brodo (1995) noted that lichenan had a strong affinity for Congo Red, although the staining properties were not sufficiently specific to allow identification of this substance. Examples of stains which have been used in lichenology are given below.

Congo Red
1% w/v solution in distilled water.

This stain is often used in conjunction with K. A drop of each may be mixed on a microscope slide and the material mounted into it. Excess stain may be removed by drawing more K under the coverslip by means of a piece of tissue paper. Congo Red stains hyphal walls and is a useful general stain. Slides which can be examined again one or more times can be made, if the coverslip is attached at one side with a drop of nail varnish or glue (e.g. UHU), and the slide allowed to dry out. The slide can be re-examined by adding a drop of water.

Erythrosin
Erythrosin added to concentrated ammonia solution.

Recommended for observation of pycnidia by Coppins (1983). Pycnidia can be softened in a small drop of K on a slide for about one minute; excess K is removed with tissue paper, and a squash prepared in the erythrosin solution.

Lactophenol Cotton Blue

phenol	20 g
lactic acid (S.G. 1.21)	20 g
glycerol	40 g
distilled water	20 ml

Cotton Blue is added to the above solution until the desired intensity is reached.

Mount material in the solution, add coverslip, and warm to almost boiling point to increase take-up of the stain and to eliminate air bubbles. When air is expelled and the slide is cooled, it can be ringed with two coats of nail varnish or a proprietary agent such as Glyceel; such a preparation can last several years. If heat is not used, the stain will be taken up, but more slowly. In most tissues the hyphal contents but not the hyphal walls are stained. Fine measurements, such as the dimensions of spores and hyphae, should not be made in this reagent as it causes shrinkage. Addition of lactophenol cotton blue to preparations in K will produce gas bubbles that may destroy fine structures.

CAUTION: phenol is implicated as a carcinogen. It should be handled with care, used in a fume cupboard, and care should be taken not to boil slides. Phenol may be omitted from the above formula to reduce health risks. Some mycologists use Cotton Blue as a 1% w/v solution in lactic acid alone.

Chlorazol Black
A 1% solution of chlorazol black in water was used by Nash et al. (1990) to observe details of ascus dehiscence. Hymenial sections were treated for approximately 30 seconds with C diluted to one-third normal strength. Sections were transferred to a 'basic solution' of the stain and heating to near boiling for c. 1 minute. The sections were transferred to a drop of 2% acetic acid, causing instantaneous precipitation of the stain.

A solution of stain in c. 2.5% KOH appears to be adequate. The procedure can be carried out on an open microscope slide; after heating the stain is precipitated by adding a small drop of acid, and a coverslip is added.

Toluidine Blue
A 1% solution in distilled water was used by Grube (1993) to investigate structure of asci and vegetative hyphae. The stain shows either blue (orthochromatic) or reddish to violet (metachromatic) colours in different tissues. A 0.05% solution of toluidine blue in a 0.05% solution of sodium borate in water was used by Common & Brodo (1995) to investigate thallus anatomy.

Brilliant Cresyl Blue
A 0.1-1% solution in tap water was recommended by Baral (1992). The stain shows colour reactions similar to toluidine blue. It was used to investigate the asci and vegetative hyphae of non-lichenized lichenicolous species by Roux & Triebel (1994) and Roux et al. (1995).

6. MICROCRYSTALLIZATION

The microcrystallization method relies on the characteristic crystal forms assumed by lichen substances when recrystallised in a suitable solvent. The method has been almost completely superseded by the more sensitive and reliable methods of thin-layer chromatography (TLC), but the technique is still useful for a small number of lichen compounds, and can be used by those without access to TLC. The method is of most use where a small number of taxa of known chemistry are to be separated. Mixtures of substances may be difficult to resolve, and minor substances may be undetectable. In a few cases different substances may combine as crystals of a single form, for instance the characteristic crystals formed by mixtures of sekikaic and homosekikaic acids, which were initially regarded as representing a single compound.

Microcrystallization is a useful method to distinguish some pairs of compounds which separate poorly in commonly used TLC systems, for instance gyrophoric and lecanoric acids (Fig. 2), and barbatic and diffractaic acids (Brodo & Hawksworth 1977). Other microchemical tests which produce characteristic crystals are the K tests for norstictic acid and polyporic acid (see Section 2.3).

6.1. Reagents

Solvents GAW and GE are the most frequently used solvents, and are relatively safe to use, but not all substances will crystallize in these. Care should be taken when using An, *o*T, Py and Q, as they contain toxic substances. Proportions by volume unless indicated. The choice of solvent will normally depend on which substances are expected in the sample, and will be indicated by published references to microcrystal tests of those substances.

GAW

glycerol	1
ethanol (Industrial Methylated Spirit)	1
water	1

GE

glycerol	3
glacial acetic acid	1

An

aniline	1
glycerol	2
ethanol	2

*o*T

o-toluidine	1
glycerol	2
ethanol	2

Py

pyridine	1
glycerol	1
water	3

Q

quinoline	1
ethanol	2
glycerol	2

KK

potassium hydroxide (KOH)	5 g

| potassium carbonate (K_2CO_3) | 20 g |
| distilled water | 100 ml |

6.2. Methods

1. Extract a fragment of lichen in a small test tube in a drop or two of acetone.
2. Transfer the extract to a microscope slide on a hot plate, using a capillary tube, so that a solid deposit of lichen substances is produced. Alternatively, place the lichen fragment on a slide on a hot plate at *c*. 50-70° C, and add acetone one drop at a time, allowing each drop to dry before adding the next. When a solid residue has built up, allow to dry, and brush away lichen fragments with a soft brush.
3. If the residue is thin, it may be an advantage to scrape it into one place using a razor blade.
4. Add a small amount of solvent, and cover with a small coverslip (10-18 mm square); the drop of solvent can be added to the coverslip before lowering onto the residue.
5. For solvents GAW and GE, warm the slide carefully on a hot plate or over a spirit lamp until some of the residue has dissolved. The slide can be warmed until bubbles just appear under the coverslip, but must not be overheated. The other solvents are normally not heated, but sometimes better results are obtained with heat.
6. Allow the slide to cool at room temperature.
7. After 5-10 minutes, observe with low power of the compound microscope. Search all parts of the preparation, as crystals may form near the edge as well as near the undissolved residue. Some substances take longer to crystallize, and the slide should be re-examined at intervals of up to 24 hours.

6.3. Problems and interpretation

If no crystals are apparent then either lichen substances are absent, an incorrect solvent has been used, or the substance has failed to crystallize due to problems with preparation.

Problems with the method include:

Too much solvent, which dilutes the residue. Small coverslips (10 × 10 mm) are recommended, especially when only a small amount of substance is available.

Overheating or underheating of the preparation.

Incorrect solvent.

Presence of lichen fragments or rock crystals may prevent crystallization.

Two or more substances are present, forming combined complexes of uncertain shape. Repeat using a range of solvents, and adequate resolution should be possible in one of them.

The coverslip should not be moved after heating.

Solvent needs to be replaced. Old solutions, impurities and moisture may cause aberration or prevent crystallization.

6.4. Identification

Identification of crystals is achieved by comparison with published photographs of crystals in various solvents. Photographs of microcrystals of numerous substances were published by Huneck & Yoshimura (1996), and other photographs can be found in works including Hale (1974), Thomson (1967, *Cladonia*), Brodo & Hawksworth (1977, diffractaic, barbatic and psoromic acids), and Orange (1992, *Cladonia chlorophaea* group). References to microcrystal tests of specific compounds can be traced through Culberson (1969, 1970) and Culberson *et al.* (1977). The method should be practised on material containing known substances. The form of the crystals depends on the solvent used and to some extent on the concentration of the substance, but the basic forms can usually be discerned. Care should be taken not to confuse undissolved substance (which may be crystalline but without characteristic form) with recrystallized substance. Microcrystal preparations cannot be stored, but begin to degenerate within hours or days.

Gyrophoric acid and lecanoric acid are difficult to distinguish from each other using thin-layer chromatography (section 9.6.1), but a microcrystal test can be used to distinguish these substances if one of them is known to be present (Fig. 2). Lecanoric acid produces clusters of well-developed long, curved crystals in GAW. Gyrophoric acid produces small clusters of short crystals in GAW, but the result is often poor, particularly if other substances are present. In GE, gyrophoric acid may appear as small wispy clusters of fine crystals, or as rounded aggregations of very small crystals (do not confuse with undissolved substance, which can appear as rounded aggregations in both substances). Lecanoric acid in GE forms clusters of needle-like crystals, but these are less well-developed than in GAW. These tests can be used to distinguish *Punctelia borreri* (gyrophoric acid) from *P. subrudecta* (lecanoric acid); use GAW first, which should easily distinguish lecanoric acid, if present. If there is no result in GAW, repeat the test; if the second test is also negative, try GE.

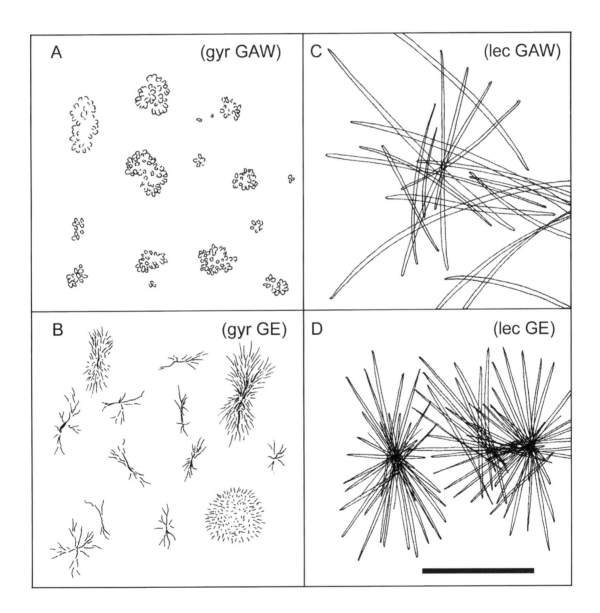

FIG. 2. Crystals of gyrophoric acid and lecanoric acid (diagrammatic). A, gyrophoric acid in GAW, B, gyrophoric acid in GE, C, lecanoric acid in GAW, D, lecanoric acid in GE. Scale = 50 μm.

6.5. Extinction angle

In cases where two substances produce crystals of similar appearance, the optical properties of the crystals may provide a useful distinction. Some crystals cause a shift in the plane of polarisation of transmitted light. If a crystal of such a compound is rotated between crossed polars (see Section 7) it will appear alternately bright and dark with every 90° turn. At those positions where the crystal appears dark (in extinction) the angle between a particular axis of the crystal and the plane of polarization of the filter is known as the extinction angle.

Perlatolic acid and imbricaric acid form long, more or less straight crystals in GE, which have extinction angles of 0° and 45° respectively with respect to their long axis (Fig. 3). The accurate measurement of the extinction angle requires the use of a petrological microscope, but these compounds can be distinguished by observing a single crystal while rotating the preparation on the microscope stage between crossed polars. The angle of the crystal with respect to the plane of polarization can be roughly estimated.

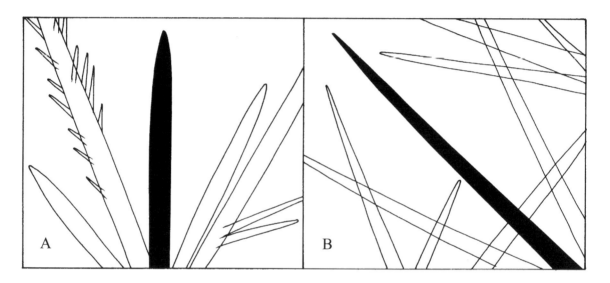

FIG. 3. Crystals of perlatolic acid (A) and imbricaric acid (B) in GE, viewed between crossed polars (diagrammatic). The central crystal (shown dark) is in extinction. The planes of polarization of the two filters are vertical and horizontal.

7. POLARIZED LIGHT

The presence, distribution, size and solubility of crystals and granules within apothecial tissues are an important feature in some discocarp genera such as *Lecanora* and *Pertusaria*, and in pyrenocarp genera such as *Porina*. Many species in widely differing genera have some crystal inclusions but as yet the significance of their shape, size and constancy is poorly known.

Crystalline material may often be overlooked, and minute crystalline granules are difficult to distinguish from oil droplets or other non-crystalline material using ordinary light. Crystalline material is made more easily visible in water mounts of tissue sections by using polarizing filters. One filter is placed between the light source and the specimen, and a second filter between the specimen and the eyepiece lenses of the microscope. When one filter is rotated relative to the other, a point is reached where the planes of polarization of the filters are at 90° to each other ('crossed polars' or 'crossed Nicols'), and most of the light from the microscope lamp is excluded. Crystalline material causes a rotation of the plane of polarization of light reaching the specimen, and the material appears bright against a dark background when viewed under crossed polars. Note that the hyphal walls of certain tissues are also refractive and appear bright under crossed polars.

It is not necessary to use expensive filters; polarising film which can be cut with scissors is adequate. If there is a filter holder within the barrel of the microscope, a piece of the film can be cut to size and inserted, or it can be placed inside the eyepiece. A second piece can be placed over the light source. One of the filters can be rotated to achieve crossed polars.

In the '*Lecanora subfusca* group', crystals occur in the apothecium, and their size, location, and solubility in K and nitric acid are important taxonomic features (Table 11). Thin sections are mounted first in water and examined both with normal light and using crossed polars. Solubility is best demonstrated by infusion of K solution through the preparation while observing the preparation under the microscope. Any insoluble crystals will still be visible with crossed polars. Nitric acid should not be brought near microscope objectives, and it is better to place a section in a drop of acid for a few seconds, then wash and remount it in water. Brodo (1984) used concentrated nitric acid, but 50% nitric acid (i.e. a 1:1 mixture of concentrated nitric acid and water) is adequate and less hazardous.

Crystalline granules occur in the epihymenium of some species of the *L. subfusca* group, and are always soluble in K. Brodo (1984) distinguished four basic types of epihymenium in this group:

1. *chlarotera*-type: crystalline granules on surface, only rarely extending between tips of paraphyses; granules coarse, the shape discernible at × 400 magnification, soluble in concentrated nitric acid; pigment present or absent (Fig. 4A).
2. *pulicaris*-type: crystalline granules on surface and extending up to 20 µm between tips of paraphyses; granules fine, shape not discernible at × 400 magnification, insoluble in concentrated nitric acid; pigment present, brown to olivaceous (Fig. 4B).
3. *glabrata*-type: no granules, pigment clear reddish brown (Fig. 4C).
4. *gangaleoides*-type: no granules, pigment olive or green.

The apothecial margin (amphithecium) of the *L. subfusca* group contains coarse crystals in the medulla, which are insoluble in K, but soluble in nitric acid. In addition the amphithecial cortex contains small crystals which are soluble in K but insoluble in nitric acid (resembling the granules in the *pulicaris*-type of epihymenium). Brodo (1984) distinguished four types of amphithecium in the *L. subfusca* group:

1. *pulicaris*-type: very large crystals in the medulla, usually in clumps (Fig.4D).
2. *campestris*-type: small crystals entirely or partially filling the medulla, but not entering the cortex (Fig. 4E).
3. *allophana*-type: small crystals extending from the medulla into the cortex (Fig. 4F).

In some species it is useful to dissolve the cortical crystals in K so that the distribution of the medullary crystals can be seen more easily. Amphithecial crystals vary in abundance, and it may be necessary to examine more than one apothecium.

Note that the drawings of amphithecia in Fig. 4D-F represent individual specimens and do not show the full range of variation of each type.

TABLE 11. Epihymenial and amphithecial types in selected western European species of the *Lecanora subfusca* group.

species	epihymenium	amphithecium
L. pulicaris	pulicaris	pulicaris
L. sinuosa	pulicaris	pulicaris
L. chlarotera	chlarotera	pulicaris
L. rugosella	chlarotera	pulicaris
L. cenisia	chlarotera	pulicaris
L. argentata	glabrata	pulicaris
L. campestris	glabrata	campestris
L. laevis	glabrata	campestris
L. horiza	glabrata	campestris/allophana
L. allophana	glabrata	allophana
L. gangaleoides	gangaleoides	pulicaris

Many of the crystalline deposits found in lichens are composed of calcium oxalate, for instance the pruina on the thallus surface of many species (note that not all pruina is crystalline). Aptroot *et al.* (2009) used '25% H_2SO_4' to identify calcium oxalate crystals in the thallus of *Herpothallon*: under the microscope, crystals dissolved and then recrystallized as needle-shaped crystals of calcium sulphate. Calcium oxalate dissolves in 2% hydrochloric acid but not in 5% acetic acid (glacial acetic acid: water 5: 95) (Yasue 1969). Yasue identified calcium oxalate in mammalian tissue by a combination of methods, including the following: tissue sections were immersed in 5% acetic acid for 30 minutes to remove calcium carbonate and calcium phosphate, then immersed in 5% silver nitrate in water for 10-20 minutes, rinsed thoroughly and immersed in a saturated solution of dithiooxamide (rubeanic acid) in 70% alcohol (IMS) containing 2 drops of strong ammonia solution per 100 ml; sections were rinsed in 50% alcohol. Calcium oxalate deposits appeared dark brown or black. This method is not specific for calcium oxalate, and would produce positive results with certain other metal salts.

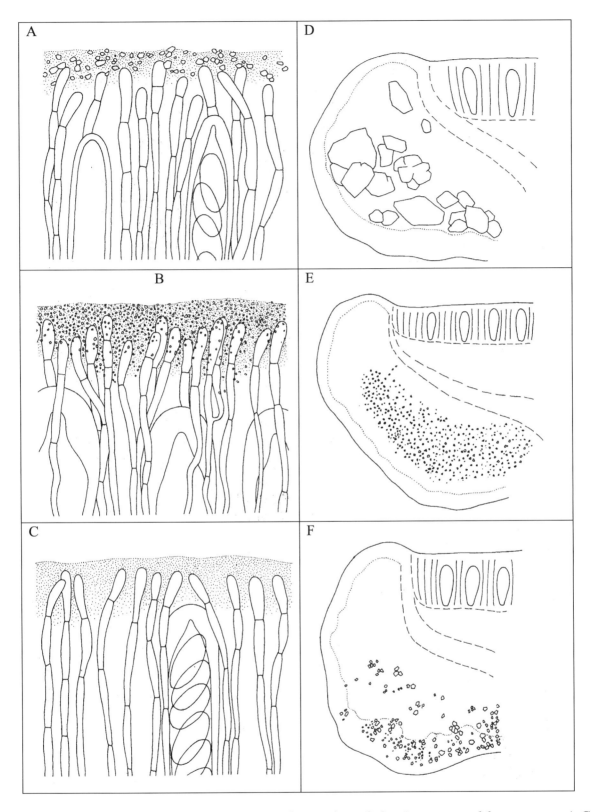

FIG. 4. Epihymenial and amphithecial types in species of the *Lecanora subfusca* group. A-C, epihymenia (schematic): A. *Lecanora chlarotera* (*chlarotera*-type), B. *L. pulicaris* (*pulicaris*-type), C. *L. argentata* (*glabrata*-type). D-F, amphithecia, showing location of KOH-insoluble crystals (KOH-soluble crystals in cortex omitted): D. *L. argentata* (*pulicaris*-type), E. *L. campestris* (*campestris*-type), F. *L. allophana* (*allophana*-type).

8. ULTRA-VIOLET FLUORESCENCE

An important number of lichen substances show a wide range of colour and intensity of fluorescence under long-wave ultra-violet (350 nm). In some cases the UV fluorescence may be characteristic *in situ* in the lichen, whilst in other species fluorescence is only revealed during the processing of TLC plates (see section 9).

Thallus fluorescence is produced either by pigments in the cortex, such as xanthones, which fluoresce shades of yellow, orange and red, or by depsides and depsidones concentrated in the medulla, which fluoresce blue to white. Table 12. gives examples of lichen thalli which are UV + . As several different substances are involved in fluorescence it is important that specific identification is carried out using TLC.

Certain closely related taxa may be rapidly separated by direct examination of thalli under UV light. Unsuspected mixed collections of *Cladonia*, for instance, can be rapidly revealed.

Mains operated UV lamps are ideal. Inexpensive battery operated UV lamps are also available. Although these are not as intense as mains operated lamps, they can perform well and give comparable results; they can also be used in the field. Fluorescence is best studied in a darkened room. Beware of visible light produced by the lamp and reflected by the specimen, this can appear as a dull mauve colour which can be confused with fluorescence. One should be especially careful when testing a white medulla against a dark cortex. If there is any doubt about whether fluorescence is occurring, it is a good idea to compare with a known UV + species such as *Cladonia portentosa*. Cortical pigments can mask fluoresence, so it may be necessary to abrade the surface to expose the medulla. If specimens are to be mounted on card in the herbarium, it is necessary to choose card with a UV – surface, so that the fluorescence of the card does not mask that of the lichen. Where specimens have been mounted on UV + card, the specimen should be viewed through a hole in a piece of black paper so that only light from the specimen can be seen. When specimens have been housed in a paper packet, the edges may be contaminated with UV + material from the paper, although this is rarely likely to be confused with fluorescence due to the specimen.

When using filter paper methods for spot tests (see Section 2.2), the UV fluorescence characteristics of the spot may not be reliable, as the fluorescence of a UV + substance may be masked by other substances in the extract.

CAUTION: short wave UV (which is not used in examining whole thalli) is damaging to the eyes and must not be used without appropriate protection. When using mains operated lamps with both long and short-wave tubes, make sure that the long wave tube is switched on when examining lichen thalli. For extra protection, appropriate protective goggles should be worn whenever UV lamps are used. Although the biological hazards of long-wave UV (UVA) are low, there are maximum permissible exposure limits (Beaver 1992).

TABLE 12. Examples of lichen thalli showing UV fluorescence			
species	tissue	colour	major substances responsible
Arctoparmelia incurva	medulla	bluish white	alectoronic and α-collatolic acid
Bacidia viridifarinosa	surface	orange	coronatone
Buellia pulverea	surface	faint orange	alectorialic acid
Caloplaca (orange species)	surface	orange	parietin
Candelariella spp.	surface	orange	calycin
Cladonia crispata	medulla	white	squamatic acid
Cladonia callosa	medulla	white	grayanic acid
Cladonia glauca	medulla	white	squamatic acid
Cladonia portentosa	medulla	bluish white	perlatolic acid
Cladonia squamosa var. *squamosa*	surface and medulla	white	squamatic acid
Cladonia uncialis ssp. *biuncialis*	surface	white	squamatic acid
Dibaeis baeomyces	surface	pale orange	baeomycesic and squamatic acid
Fuscidea kochiana	medulla	bluish white	divaricatic acid
Fuscidea lightfootii	medulla and soralia	bluish white	divaricatic acid
Lecanora alboflavida	surface	orange	xanthones
Lecanora epanora	surface	orange	epanorin and rhizocarpic acid
Lecanora expallens	soralia	dark orange-brown	xanthones
Lecanora quercicola	surface	pale greyish white	unknown pigments
Lecidella elaeochroma	surface	orange	xanthones
Loxospora elatina	medulla	bluish white	unknowns
Mycoblastus caesius	medulla and soralia	bluish white	perlatolic acid
Ophioparma ventosa	medulla	white	divaricatic acid
Parmotrema arnoldii	medulla	bluish white	alectoronic and α-collatolic acid
Pertusaria flavida	surface	vivid orange	thiophaninic acid
Pertusaria hymenea	surface	orange	thiophaninic acid
Pertusaria pertusa	surface	orange	coronatone
Physconia enteroxantha	medulla	orange	unknown pigment
Psilolechia lucida	surface	yellow-ochre	rhizocarpic acid
Pyrenula dermatodes	surface	vivid orange	xanthones
Pyrrhospora quernea	surface	dull orange-brown	thiophanic acid and isoarthothelin

TABLE 12 (continued). Examples of lichen thalli showing UV fluorescence			
Schismatomma umbrinum	medulla and soralia	intense ice-blue (fresh), yellowish white on storage	unknown
Sphaerophorus globosus	medulla	white	sphaerophorin
Stereocaulon evolutum	medulla	white	lobaric acid
Tephromela atra	medulla	bluish white	alectoronic and α-collatolic acid
Xanthoria parietina	surface	bright orange	parietin

9. THIN-LAYER CHROMATOGRAPHY

9.1. Introduction

Thin-layer chromatography (TLC) is a relatively simple and inexpensive technique which can be used by anyone with access to basic laboratory facilities. Lichen samples are extracted in acetone, and the extract is spotted onto glass or aluminium plates coated with silica gel. The plate is placed in a sealed tank so that the base of the plate is immersed in a shallow layer of a specific mixture of organic solvents. The different lichen substances present in the sample are separated from each other during the passage of solvent through the silica gel layer, and are later made visible by spraying with sulphuric acid or other reagents. The resulting spots are provisionally identified by their colour and relative position, and positive identification is achieved by running further samples against controls of known chemistry. Examples of chromatograms of species in a genus (*Lepraria*) where chemistry is important for identification are shown in Figs. 7 and 8.

9.2. Solvent systems

Several solvent systems are widely used for routine analysis of lichen samples, each giving different results. In addition, there are a number of solvent systems for specialist use. It is recommended that for initial analysis of samples, solvent system C or G is used, as these are stable and reliable. If the purpose of the analysis is simply to distinguish between taxa whose chemistry is well known, it may be sufficient to use only one solvent system. For more critical work, it is necessary to use more than one solvent system, as a single system may not separate all the compounds that are present. It is recommended that samples should be run in three different systems to fully characterize an unidentified substance. Further analyses in specialist solvent sytems may be necessary to separate certain compounds which show very similar characteristics in the routinely used solvent sytems.

The precise formulation of some of the solvent sytems has changed over the years, partly as a result of the replacement of some components by less hazardous alternatives. Different formulations of the same system are likely to give slightly differing results.

Solvent systems for routine use:

A: toluene/ dioxan/ acetic acid   180: 45: 5 (Culberson & Ammann 1979). This is a stable and useful system. System C is preferred for routine use as it is said to be slightly less hazardous.

B: hexane/ methyl *tert*-butyl ether/ formic acid 140: 72: 18 (Culberson & Johnson 1982). The solvent should be replaced frequently. The original formulation of Culberson (1972) used the more hazardous diethyl ether in place of methyl *tert*-butyl ether. Arup *et al.* (1993), also for safety reasons, used the formulation cyclohexane/ methyl *tert*-butyl ether/ formic acid 130: 100: 20, and published data for its use in HPTLC.

C: toluene/ acetic acid 170: 30 (Mietsch *et al.* 1994). A stable and reliable system for general use. Culberson (1972) and several other authors used the components in the proportion of 200: 30.

G: toluene/ ethylacetate/ formic acid 139: 83: 8. A stable and reliable system for general use. Also very useful for separation of low R_f compounds such as β-orcinol depsidones, hopane terpenoids and fatty acids. It has an important role in routine analyses for most groups of compounds, for example, perlatolic and stenosporic acids can be separated in this solvent system.

Specialist solvent systems:

D: butanol/ acetone/ water 150: 30: 60 (Culberson & Ammann 1979, as solvent system 'E'). Used for the separation of low R_f β-orcinol depsidones.

E: cyclohexane/ ethyl acetate 75: 25   (Elix & Crook 1992). Used for the separation of compounds of high R_f in the standard systems, including atranorin, chloroatranorin, pannarin, physciosporin and xanthones. Prepare fresh daily.

EA: diethyl ether/ acetic acid 100: 1 (Culberson & Ammann 1979, as solvent system 'D'). Used for the separation of lecanoric and gyrophoric acids. The solvent must be freshly prepared for each session. Diethyl ether is an extremely flammable solvent which must be handled with particular care. It cannot be replaced by methyl *tert*-butyl ether in this solvent system.

EH: diethylether/ hexane 90: 30 (for terpenoids) (White & James 1985). Used for the separation of terpenoids. Prepare fresh for each run.

EHF: diethylether/ hexane/ formic acid 300/ 100/ 3 (Tønsberg & Holtan-Hartwig 1983). Used for separation of terpenoids.

F: ethyl acetate/ cyclohexane 1: 1 (Elix & Crook 1992). Used as an additional solvent for xanthones. Separates atranorin and chloroatranorin.

H: cyclohexane/ chloroform/ methyl ethyl ketone 60: 30: 40 (Santesson 1967). Used by Tønsberg to separate atranorin and chloratranorin, and usnic and isousnic acids.

HEF: hexane/ ethyl acetate/ formic acid 139: 83: 8 (White & James 1986). Used to separate high R_f compounds such as perlatolic and stenosporic acids.

J: dichloromethane/ acetone 4: 1 (Hanko 1983). Used for separation of xanthones.

OH: ethyl acetate/ methanol/ ammonia (S.G. 0.91) 75: 20: 5 (Archer 1993). Used for separation of orcinol *para*-depsides in *Pertusaria*.

9.3. Reagents for visualization of spots

<u>1. 10% sulphuric acid</u>

A mixture of concentrated sulphuric acid (i.e. 98% sulphuric acid, density 1.84) and distilled water in the proportion 1: 9. (Add acid carefully to water, <u>not</u> the other way around).

This is the most commonly used reagent; see below for details of use.

<u>2. 3-Methyl-2-benzothiazolone hydrazone hydrochloride (MBTH)</u> (Archer 1978).

Dissolve 0.1 g MBTH in 10 ml water, and dilute to 100 ml with methyl alcohol.

The use of MBTH is usually followed by potassium ferricyanide (see below).

<u>3. Potassium ferricyanide</u> (Archer 1978)

A mixture of the two following solutions:

a. 0.5% potassium ferricyanide solution:

potassium ferricyanide	1.0 g
distilled water	200 ml

b. 5 N potassium hydroxide solution:

potassium hydroxide	14.05 g
distilled water	50 ml

This reagent is used in conjunction with MBTH (see below for method of use).

4. Magnesium acetate
A 2% solution in ethanol (Industrial Methylated Spirit).
Sprayed or painted onto plate. Used only for quinones.

5. Triethylamine
The TLC plate is exposed to triethylamine vapour for a few minutes in a closed tank. Used only for quinones.

9.4. Preparation

Solvents and developing tank:
The solvent mixtures should be made up in a fume cupboard as a protection against harmful vapours. Glassware should be clean and completely dry. Only small quantities of solvents should be made up at one time as they deteriorate in storage. Solvent system B is particularly prone to evapouration, and tends to give poor results after a relatively short period of storage.

Pour solvent into the tank to form a shallow layer approximately 10 mm deep in the base. When using solvent systems A and B place a piece of clean blotting paper at the back of the tank so that the solvent can soak through it. This assists uniform vapour saturation and ensures free running of the solvent front. Seal the lid of the tank with silicone grease. Allow the tank to come to equilibrium for two hours before use. Some solvent systems will remain usable in the tank for several days, but R_f values will gradually become unreliable, and the solvent (and blotting paper) should be replaced.

Plates:
TLC plates are usually 20 × 20 cm in size, and made of glass or aluminium coated with a layer of silica gel. Glass plates must be used for the study of fatty acids (and for critical study of xanthones, see Section 9.6.3). For normal use, plates should contain an indicator which fluoresces under short wave UV.

Draw a line 20 mm from the base of the plate using a soft pencil. Mark this line at 10 mm intervals; this gives starting position for 19 samples per plate. It is convenient to cut notches at 10 mm intervals in a plastic ruler so that the starting positions are marked on the base line when it is drawn. Another line may be drawn 130 mm from the base of the plate to represent the finishing line of the solvent front, although some workers allow most or all of the plate to be used. For critical work, avoid using the outer positions on the plate, as distortion of sample spots may occur here.

If it is necessary to run only a small number of sample, plates can be cut to smaller sizes. Aluminium plates can be cut using a stout knife. Glass plates should be cut using a specially designed TLC plate cutter.

9.5. Procedure

1. Select control substances to be placed at points 3 and 7 on each plate. Norstictic acid and atranorin are useful controls for general work. Additional controls assist in establishing the R_f of unknown spots. Useful control substances can be supplied by appropriate mixtures of the following species:

Pleurosticta acetabulum: norstictic acid
Cladonia subcervicornis: fumarprotocetraric acid, atranorin
Parmelia sulcata: salazinic acid, atranorin.
Parmotrema perlatum: stictic acid, atranorin.

Additional substances used as controls by Mietsch *et al.* (1994) are listed in Table 13. It is useful to build up a collection of lichens specifically for use as controls (for instance, unwanted fragments collected for identification), to avoid repeated damage to herbarium specimens.

2. Number and record the lichens to be examined. A design for a suitable data sheet is shown in Fig. 6. It is useful to give each TLC plate a separate number to allow cross-referencing between specimen and TLC run, so that copies or photographs of the plates can be re-examined later if necessary.

3. Place small fragments of lichen in a small test tube. It is important to ensure that the sample is completely dry, and is not a mixture of species. Samples from crustose species should be carefully removed under a binocular microscope to prevent inadvertent mixing of two or more species. Crusts on rock can be scraped away with the point of a scalpel, and the fragments caught on a clean slip of paper. Samples of foliose and fruticose species should be pushed well down into the bottom of the tube to maximise contact with the solvent when this is added.

4. To each sample add one drop of cold acetone, or just sufficient to moisten the sample; excess solvent should be avoided. Absorbent material, such as *Lepraria*, may require additional drops.

5. Using a clean capillary tube for each sample, transfer some of the acetone extract in each tube to the corresponding numbered point on the TLC plate. If necessary, add an extra drop of acetone if the first has dried out. Allow the spot to dry between each application. The spots on the base line of the plate should be kept as small as possible to minimise the likelihood of undue spreading and merging on the developed plates; at least three applications per spot are recommended to give adequate results, but heavier or lighter loading may be necessary in some cases, e.g. heavier for *Alectoria*, *Bryoria* and *Usnea* species, and lighter for some species containing large amounts of gyrophoric, lecanoric, stictic or norstictic acids. If the concentration of a particular lichen substance is known to be low in a given species, or if trace amounts of accessory substances are critical for determination, the acetone extract may be boiled in the test tube using an electric hotplate.

The test tubes may be re-used only if they are thoroughly washed and rinsed in warm acetone. Used capillary tubes should be discarded.

CAUTION: acetone is flammable and naked flames must be avoided.

6. When using solvent systems B and C, it is recommended that the plates (with the samples spotted onto the baseline) should be placed in a tank containing 60% formic acid for 5 minutes (solvent B) or glacial acetic acid for 10 minutes (solvent C); the plate should be supported above the level of the acid. This allows equilibration with the vapour, allowing uniform travel of the solvent front and preventing the development of secondary solvent fronts.

7. Place the prepared plate carefully into a developing tank containing the chosen solvent system, so that the base is immersed, and the plate is upright or nearly so. When using solvent systems A or B, the silica gel layer on the plate should face the filter paper in the tank. Leave until the solvent front has reached the finishing line (or the top of the plate, whichever is to be used). Plates will take from 30 minutes to more than an hour to run, depending on the age of the solvent system and the temperature and other atmospheric conditions prevailing at the time.

8. Remove the plate and dry in a fume cupboard. The more volatile solvents evapourate in a few minutes, but 10-30 minutes is advisable to remove less volatile components such as acetic and formic acids. If fatty acids are to be investigated, the plate should be allowed to dry thoroughly in a warm room until no smell of acetic acid or formic acid can be detected (preferably overnight), otherwise traces of acid create a mottled effect when sprayed with water, interfering with the spots caused by fatty acids.

9. Examine plates by daylight for pigments and note their colour and position.

10. View the plate under short wave UV. Aromatic lichen substances show up as dark spots against a bright green fluorescent background (assuming that plates containing a fluorescent indicator are being used). Draw around the spots with a soft pencil. Even faint spots should also be indicated (some indicate very faint spots by a convex line drawn over the top, rather than a complete line). A few compounds show fluoresence at this stage, and this may be noted on the plate as a minor character for identification.

In special cases, if the spots below R_f class 4 (below norstictic acid) are complex or crowded, the plates can be returned to the solvent and re-run to increase the separation. However, if this is done then the spots above R_f 4 will be of no value. Alternatively, an additional plate should be run in solvent system G to allow better separation of these low R_f spots.

CAUTION: the eyes must be protected from harmful radiation when using UV (especially short wave), even though the user is not looking directly into the lamp. Suitable spectacles must be used, or a sheet of clear perspex may be hung in front of the lamp and TLC plate during viewing.

11. View the plate under long wave UV, and note the strength and colour of any fluorescence by writing on the plate with a soft pencil. Indicate any new spots (that did not appear in short wave UV) with a dotted line. The fluorescence of faint spots may be increased in some cases by viewing the plate (glass only) when it is held *over* the UV source.

12. If fatty acids are suspected, spray the plate with a fine spray of water until it is translucent. Allow to dry slowly. If fatty acids are present they will gradually appear as opaque white spots against a translucent background; as the plate dries further they will disappear again. Draw around the white spots and indicate them as fatty acids (e.g. by drawing a cross or an 'f' in the centre of each). Allow the plate to dry thoroughly. More than gentle heat is not recommended as it may cause blistering of the silica gel surface later in the process.

This stage can be omitted if information about fatty acids is not required, or if they are unknown in the taxa being investigated. Examples of lichens containing fatty acids include *Tuckermanopsis chlorophylla* (protolichesterinic acid), *Lecanora muralis* (muronic and murolic acid complexes), *Flavoparmelia caperata* (caperatic acid), *Pertusaria albescens* (unidentified fatty acids), *Pycnothelia papillaria* (lichesterinic and protolichesterinic acids) and *Usnea hirta* (muronic and murolic acid complexes).

13. Apply 10% sulphuric acid by means of a spray (in a suitable fume cupboard which is switched on), or by painting directly onto the surface with a broad bristle brush. Do not breath the spray, and avoid even small splashes onto clothing. The plate should be thoroughly moistened but preferably not dripping. Place the plate in a preheated oven at 110°C for approximately 10 minutes, until the the spot colours are completely developed. Prolonged heating, or too high a temperature, will cause colours to be dulled and the plate to turn brownish.

In special cases, alternative reagents may be used to visualize the spots, including C, PD or MBTH (see below). For safety reasons, PD should be applied by brush and not sprayed. As in the case of thallus spot tests, C and KC reactions are fleeting and easily missed. It is possible to apply reagents to individual spots, although reactions are often weak compared to the whole thallus. Scrape away the treated spot and develop the remainder of the plate with sulphuric acid.

14. Remove the plate from the oven. New spots of a purplish tone may have appeared during heating; these are terpenoids (see below). Note the colour of all the spots by writing on the plate with a soft pencil. Colours should be noted soon after the plate is developed. Next, examine the plate under long wave UV and note the strength and colour of any fluorescence.

It is often important to monitor any change in colour of the spots after a few minutes, several hours, and even after two to three days or more, as the changes are characteristic of some substances. For example, barbatic acid can be distinguished from diffractaic acid as the outer part of the orange-yellow spot of barbatic acid becomes dark rusty brown after 24 hours or more. The diffractaic acid spot will eventually turn deep mahogany brown after 7 days or more.

15. The developed plates can be stored, but the colours will continue to change or fade, and the silica gel layer will eventually break down. It is useful to photocopy or photograph freshly developed plates, so that they can be referred to again later. Digital images of plates can be saved using a flatbed scanner (Egan 2001).

Use of alternative agents to visualize spots
MBTH
In place of step 5. in the procedure above, spray plate with MBTH solution, and allow to dry in a fume cupboard. Observe plate under long-wave UV. Compounds with an aldehyde group and a hydroxy group in *ortho* position (Fig. 5A) give bright yellow or orange fluorescent spots.

The use of MBTH is usually followed by potassium ferricyanide. After MBTH has been applied to the plate and fluorescence observed, spray the plate with potassium ferricyanide solution. Phenolic compounds, usually with a free position *para* to a phenolic hydroxy group (Fig. 5B), give orange, red, brown or violet colours.

Note that unqualified references in the literature to the colours produced by MBTH refer to the colours produced by the use of MBTH and potassium ferricyanide in succession. The use of either reagent alone does not produce coloured spots (other than the fluorescent spots noted above).

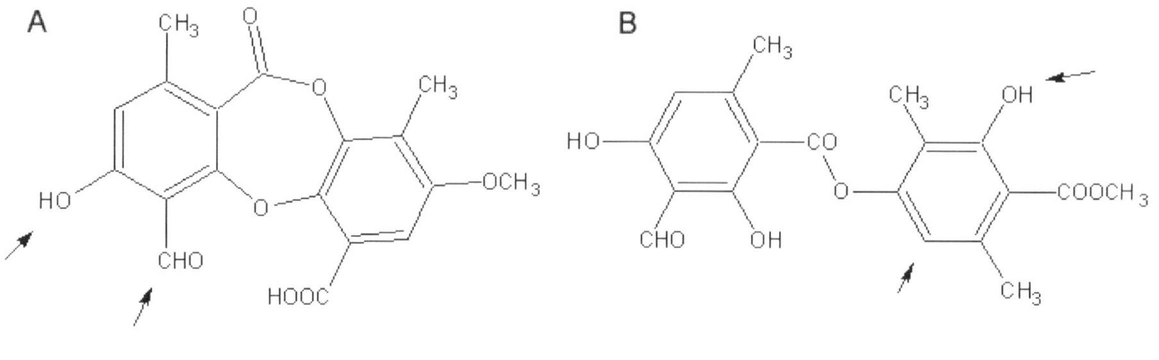

FIG. 5. Two compunds which give coloured reactions with MBTH and potassium ferricyanide. A, psoromic acid, with arrows indicating a hydroxy and an aldehyde group in *ortho* position, B. atranorin, with arrows indicating a hydroxy group *para* to a free position on the carbon ring.

9.6.1. Lecanoric and gyrophoric acids
Solvent system EA is used to separate these two substances, as an alternative to crystal tests. In this case, the R_f value of the base of the spot is important, not the top. Examples of control species are *Melanelixia fuliginosa* and *Punctelia subrudecta* for lecanoric acid and *Ochrolechia androgyna* and *Hypotrachyna revoluta* for gyrophoric acid. These commonly occurring acids are now known to be part of a series of closely related substances which may best be separated and identified by two-dimensional TLC (see Section 9.8).

Thin-layer chromatography		Plate no	

Plate: glass aluminium Spray: sulphuric acid water other none
Solvent: A B C G Operator: Date:
Subject:

specimen	substances detected		
1			
2			
3 control sample	norstictic acid	atranorin	
4			
5			
6			
7			
8			
9			
10			
11			
12			
13			
14			
15			
16			
17 control sample	norstictic acid	atranorin	
18			
19			

FIG. 6. A data sheet suitable for recording TLC information.

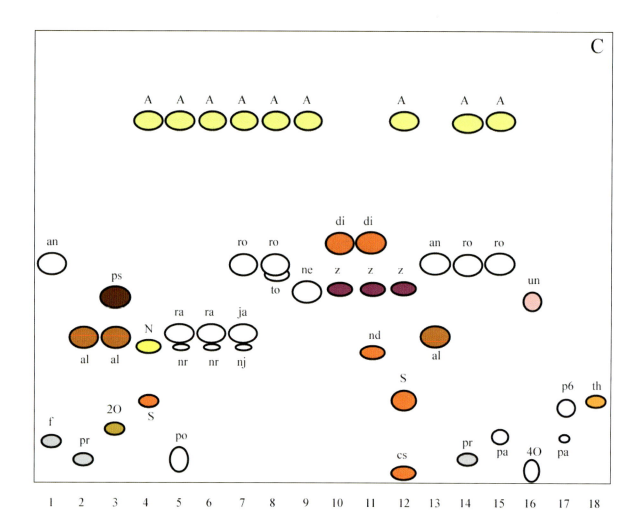

FIG. 7. Chromatogram of selected species and chemotypes of *Lepraria* in solvent system C (diagrammatic, and omitting some trace and accessory substances).

Samples: 1. *Lepraria caesioalba*, 2. *L. eburnea*, 3. *L. eburnea*, 4. control substances, 5. *L. atlantica*, 6. *L. humida*, 7. *L. jackii*, 8. *L. sylvicola*, 9. *L. rigidula*, 10. *L. incana*, 11. *L. crassissima*, 12. *L. lobificans*, 13. *L. neglecta*, 14. *L. nivalis*, 15. *L. membranacea*, 16. *L. diffusa*, 17. *L. vouauxii*, 18. *L. umbricola*.

Substances: 2O = 2'-O-demethylpsoromic acid, 4O = 4-oxypannaric acid 2-methylester, A = atranorin, un = unknown, al = alectorialic acid, an = angardianic acid, cs = constictic acid, di = divaricatic acid, f = fumarprotocetraric acid, ja = jackinic acid, N = norstictic acid, nd = nordivaricatic acid, ne =, nephrosteranic acid, nj = norjackinic acid, nr = norrangiformic acid, p6 = pannaric acid 6-methylester, pa = pannaric acid, po = porphyrilic acid, pr = protocetraric acid, ps = psoromic acid, ra = rangiformic acid, ro = roccellic acid, S = stictic acid, th = thamnolic acid, to = toensbergianic acid, z = zeorin.

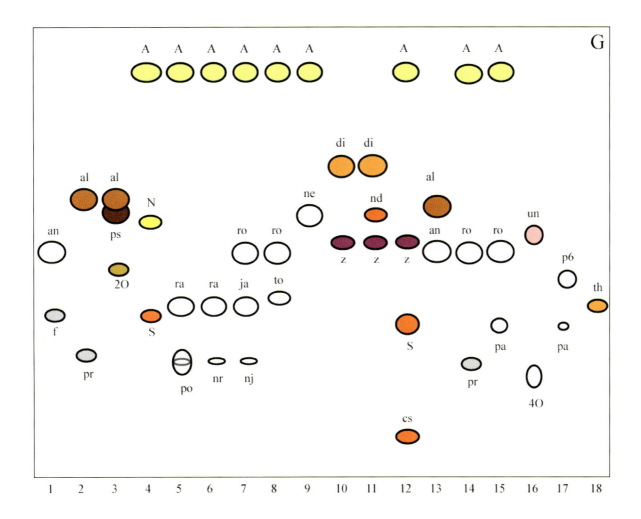

FIG. 8. Chromatogram of selected species and chemotypes of *Lepraria* in solvent system G (diagrammatic, and omitting some trace and accessory substances).

Samples: 1. *Lepraria caesioalba*, 2. *L. eburnea*, 3. *L. eburnea*, 4. control substances, 5. *L. atlantica*, 6. *L. humida*, 7. *L. jackii*, 8. *L. sylvicola*, 9. *L. rigidula*, 10. *L. incana*, 11. *L. crassissima*, 12. *L. lobificans*, 13. *L. neglecta*, 14. *L. nivalis*, 15. *L. membranacea*, 16. *L. diffusa*, 17. *L. vouauxii*, 18. *L. umbricola*.

Substances: 2O = 2'-O-demethylpsoromic acid, 4O = 4-oxypannaric acid 2-methylester, A = atranorin, un = unknown, al = alectorialic acid, an = angardianic acid, cs = constictic acid, di = divaricatic acid, f = fumarprotocetraric acid, ja = jackinic acid, N = norstictic acid, nd = nordivaricatic acid, ne =, nephrosteranic acid, nj = norjackinic acid, nr = norrangiformic acid, p6 = pannaric acid 6-methylester, pa = pannaric acid, po = porphyrilic acid, pr = protocetraric acid, ps = psoromic acid, ra = rangiformic acid, ro = roccellic acid, S = stictic acid, th = thamnolic acid, to = toensbergianic acid, z = zeorin.

9.6.2. Terpenoids

Terpenoids are characteristic or abundant in certain groups of lichens, including *Dirinaria*, *Nephroma*, *Peltigera*, *Physcia*, *Pseudocyphellaria* and *Pyxine*. Often the terpenoids occurring in a particular genus differ from those in other genera but are closely related, forming a suite of substances on the same biosynthetic pathway. Relatively few have trivial names (e.g. zeorin for hopane-6α,22-diol), and the structure of many is still unknown.

Terpenoids are easily distinguished from other substances as they are not visible until the plates have been sprayed with sulphuric acid and heated. After spraying, they are visible in daylight as purple, reddish, grey, green or brown spots or lines which typically show fluorescence in long wave UV. Their positions, colour and fluorescence colour should be noted immediately since the spots soon lose their original intensity and fade.

Particular care is needed to separate the various elements of terpenoid complexes. Aluminium plates are recommended, and ideally a range of solvent systems should be used. Extracts should be loaded heavily onto the TLC plates while using a hot plate, to ensure adequate concentration of substances. In the European species of the genus *Peltigera*, depsides which occur together with the terpenoids are of limited taxonomic value, and trailing of the depside spots may mask some of the terpenoid spots. This problem is reduced if samples are extracted using diethyl ether or hexane instead of acetone, as the depsides are much less soluble in these solvents.

Solvent system G is recommended as a reliable solvent for routine analyses where a limited number of terpenoids (up to six) are known to occur, such as in *Peltigera* and *Nephroma*. This solvent has the advantage of not requiring fresh preparation before each run. Solvents EH or EHF should also be used for more critical work as some substances may have similar R_f values and be masked if run in G alone. For critical work extracts may be run two or three times on the same 20 cm plate to give adequate separation of spots, allowing the plate to dry completely between successive runs. Where large numbers of terpenoids occur, two-dimensional TLC with known controls may be useful.

Terpenoids also occur in bark, peat, vegetable detritus and some mosses, but most of these are very different to those found in lichens. Consequently it is important to distinguish between terpenoids from the lichen and those from the substrate. If doubt occurs, extracts of the substrate should be run beside lichen extracts.

The reliable identification of terpenoids by TLC requires the use of control species. Fig. 9 shows the substances found in selected species of *Peltigera* and *Nephroma*. The pattern of terpenoids in each species is an important taxonomic character, and some species comprise several chemotypes. Note that the relative abundance of each terpenoid may vary between collections, and some are not found in every collection. Traces of additional terpenoids may be found, which are not shown in Fig. 9. The colour and fluorescence of terpenoids on freshly developed plates gives additional characters for identification. For instance phlebic acid B is green when fresh, but soon becomes a dull purple-grey; hopane-6α,7β,22-triol is purple-brown when fresh, but becomes a distinctive slaty grey. For more information on the chemistry of European *Peltigera* and *Nephroma* see Holtan-Hartwig (1993), James & White (1987) and White & James (1987).

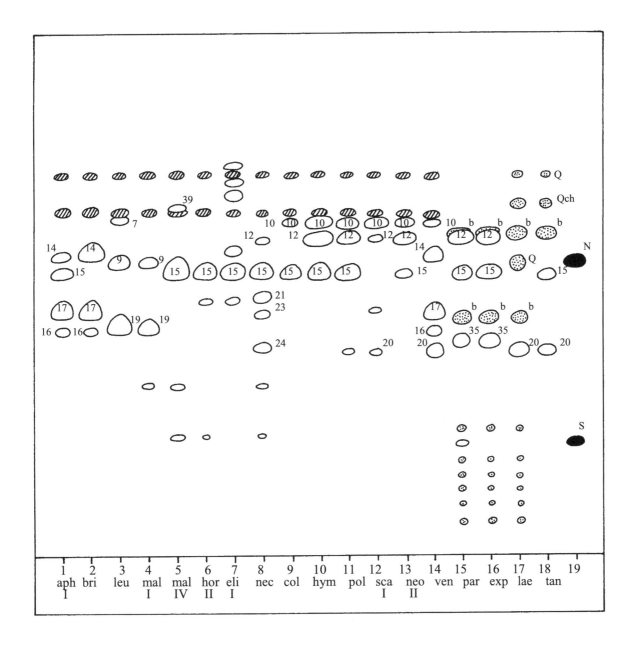

FIG. 9. Chromatogram of selected European species and chemotypes of *Peltigera* and *Nephroma*; plate run twice in G. Samples: 1. *P. aphthosa* I, 2. *P. britannica,* 3. *P. leucophlebia,* 4. *P. malacea* I; 5. *P. malacea* II, 6. *P. horizontalis* II, 7. *P. elisabethae* I, 8. *P. neckeri,* 9. *P. collina,* 10. *P. hymenina,* 11. *P. polydactylon,* 12. *P. scabrosa* I, 13. P. *neopolydactyla* II, 14. *P. venosa,* 15. *N. parile,* 16. *N. expallidum,* 17. *N. laevigatum,* 18. *N. tangeriense,* 19. controls.

Plain circles = terpenoids, hatched circles = methyl gyrophorate (lower row) and tenuiorin (upper row), dotted circles = others. Numbers refer to terpenoids, b = 'bellum-unknowns', N = norstictic acid, Q = quinones, Qch = 7-chloroemodin + emodin, S = salazinic acid. Numbering of terpenoids and chemotypes follows Holtan-Hartwig (1993); terpenoids are unnamed except for 10 = peltidactylin, 12 = dolicorrhizin, 15 = zeorin, 16 = phlebic acid A, 17 = phlebic acid B, 20 = hopane-6α,7β,22-triol, 35 = hopane-15α,22-diol.

9.6.3. Xanthones

Xanthones are widespread in lichens, and are particularly common in genera including *Lecanora*, *Lecidella*, and *Pertusaria*. Many xanthones are yellowish pigments (appearing almost colourless to pale yellow on untreated TLC plates), and many are C + or KC + orange. Spot colours following acid treatment and heating tend to be pale dirty pink to yellowish, and are rarely distinctive enough to allow identification of individual xanthones. Identification by TLC relies heavily on running lichen extracts together with control samples containing known substances. Identification by TLC alone is only reliable when chemotypes which are well understood are being investigated, and identification of xanthones in other chemotypes should be regarded as tentative until confirmed by more sophisticated methods such as HPLC.

To investigate xanthones by TLC, glass plates are essential. Samples are spotted 20 mm from the bottom of the plate as usual, but the solvent is allowed to run to within 10 mm of the top of a plate 200 mm high. Plates are examined while supported *over* a long wave UV source, to register the important fluorescence colours; no spray reagents are used. Each sample should be run in both solvent system C and J. Plates should be examined within 5 days, after which the characteristic fluorescence begins to change or fade. When fluorescence colours have been noted, plates can be sprayed with acid and heated in the normal way to identify non-xanthone substances which may be present. This method was developed by Leuckert & Knoph (1992) for recognition of chemotypes in *Lecidella*.

Solvent J gives good separation of xanthones, and good fluorescence colours. A disadvantage of solvent J is that, unlike most other solvent systems, R_f is dependent on concentration of the substance in the sample spotted onto the plate. However, the order of spots from the bottom to the top of the plate is maintained. Where a series of xanthones differing only in the number of chlorine atoms occurs, the R_f often increases with decreasing number of chlorine atoms. Plates developed in solvent C should be well dried before recording the fluorescence colours, as the colours are affected by traces of acetic acid remaining in the plate (typically more red or purple than completely dry plates). It is important to run controls together with any unknown samples, so that subtle nuances of fluorescence colour can be directly compared. Solvent systems additional to C and J may be necessary to help confirm an identification.

A few commonly occurring xanthones are listed in Appendix 1, together with non-xanthone substances. However, if the presence of xanthones is suspected, reference should be made to the more complete listing of xanthones in Appendix 2. Figs. 11 and 12 and Tables 14 and 15 give examples of species containing xanthones.

Most lichen xanthones belong to the norlichexanthone type (Fig. 10). Chlorination (substitution of a hydrogen atom by a chlorine atom) can occur at positions 2, 4, 5 or 7, and O-methylation (substitution with a OCH$_3$ group) can occur at positions 3 or 6. Of the potentially large number of compounds which could result from such substitution, approximately 50 are known to occur in lichens, and only a few have trivial names. The chemical names appear less confusing if it is realised that they refer to the pattern of substitution described above. Thus Fig. 10A shows 2,4,5-trichloro-6-O-methylnorlichexanthone, which has the trivial name of granulosin. Compounds which are O-methylated at positions 3 and 6 are considered as derivatives of lichexanthone (Fig. 10B) for purposes of nomenclature, so that the structure in Fig. 10C is named 2,7-dichlorolichexanthone.

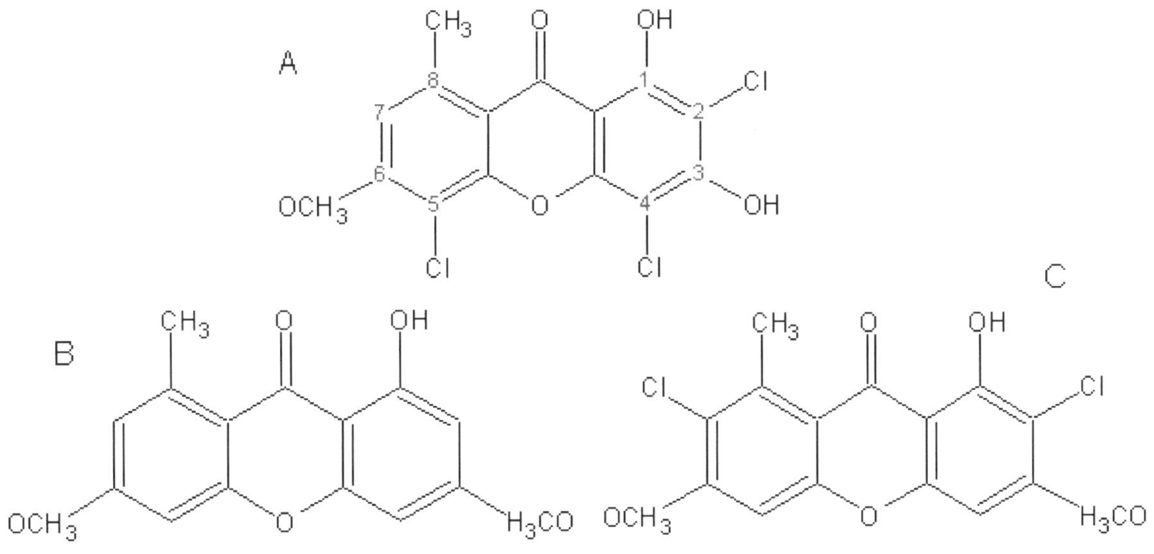

FIG. 10. Examples of xanthones. A, 2,4,5-trichloro-6-O-methylnorlichexanthone (granulosin), with carbon atoms 1-8 numbered to illustrate substitution pattern; B, lichexanthone, C, 2,7-dichlorolichexanthone.

9.6.4. Quinones

Quinones are pigmented compounds which usually appear as yellow, orange or reddish spots on untreated TLC plates (see also section 3.1 and Table 7). Identification of individual quinones is difficult, in part because they have not been so intensively studied by microchemical methods as some other classes of lichen substances. Some are poorly soluble or almost insoluble in acetone and are thus difficult to study by TLC. It may help to extract poorly soluble material for several hours in a closed vial.

The colour of the quinone spots in daylight and under long-wave UV fluorescence colour should be noted. Some quinones appear to darken and become better differentiated from each other if the plate is stored untreated for 48 hours. Instead of spraying the plate with sulphuric acid and heating, other visualizing reagents may be used to distinguish between different quinones. A 2% ethanolic solution of magnesium acetate can be sprayed or painted onto the plate. This reagent produces orange, pink or violet coloured reactions with most lichen quinones; haemoventosin gives a blue reaction, and canarione, rhodocladonic acid and polyporic acid are negative. The reagent also helps to distinguish quinones from other yellow pigments on the plate. Triethylamine is a less convenient visualizing agent; the plate is placed in a tank of triethylamine vapour for a few minutes until the quinone spots change colour. The colour and UV flourescence of the spots before and after treatment should be noted.

9.7. Interpretation of plates

Provisional identification of spots on the developed plate is achieved by comparison with published TLC data, using the R_f, colour, and fluorescence characteristics of the spot. Data for 154 commonly occurring substances are presented in Appendix 1. The provisional identification must be confirmed by running the unknown substance in three different solvent systems together with a sample known to contain the chemical in question, or preferably with a pure sample of the substance if this is available. Failure to use more than one solvent system is a source of many errors. Care must still be taken however, as some pairs of substances have almost identical TLC characteristics, or require special solvent systems to separate them. Despite these difficulties, many lichen substances are widespread and can be recognised easily with a little experience.

63

9.7.1. R_f and R_f classes

The R_f value is an expression of the distance travelled by the substance on the chromatogram relative to the solvent front. It is usually expressed multiplied by 100. Thus a substance which travels half the distance from the starting line to the solvent front has an R_f of 50. The absolute R_f measured on any occasion varies according to atmospheric conditions, the age of the solvent, the type of plate in use, and so on. However, the R_f values of substances relative to each other is more or less constant, so that they are usually expressed with reference to substances selected as standards. Norstictic acid and atranorin are two commonly used standards.

R_f classes

The R_f class is a simple method of standardizing R_f with reference to norstictic acid and atranorin controls, introduced by Culberson & Kristinsson (1969). Substances with an R_f the same as norstictic acid are defined as belonging to R_f Class 4, and substances with an R_f similar to atranorin Class 7. Substances with an R_f of 0 are Class 1. The region of the chromatogram between Classes 1 and 4 is divided equally into Classes 2 and 3, and the area between Classes 4 and 7 is divided into Classes 5 and 6. The area of the chromatogram above Class 7 is defined as Class 8.

Relative R_f values

A refinement of the standardized R_f method uses more than two control substances, each of which are assigned standard R_f values. A suitable selection of control substances is included in each chromatogram, and the measured R_f of any other substance is expressed as a relative R_f by comparison with the controls. Standard R_f values used by Mietzsch et al. (1994) are shown in Table 13. This is the standard adopted in Appendix 1, with the addition of usnic acid as a control in G. Thus, using solvent system C, a substance which travelled 40 mm from the starting line, while norstictic acid travelled 50 mm, would be considered to show an R_f of $40/50 \times 30 = 24$.

TABLE 13. Standard R_f values of control compounds, after Mietzsch et al. 1994.

compound	R_f ($\times$ 100) in solvent system:				
	A	B	C	E	G
atranorin	75	73	79	57	-
chloratranorin	74	73	81	30	-
usnic acid	70	65	71	23	88
4-O-methylhypoprotocetraric acid	35	51	45	-	61
notatic acid	24	44	38	-	55
norstictic acid	40	32	30	-	57
stictic acid	32	9	18	-	34
salazinic acid	10	7	4	-	26

9.7.2. Colour

The colour of a spot on the chromatogram is characteristic of each substance, but varies to some extent depending on factors such concentration of the substance, the solvent system used, and the degree of heating after acid treatment. Thus a large quantity of a substance may appear as a coloured spot, surrounded by a halo of another colour, representing a reduced concentration of the substance. If the substance is present only in low concentration in the lichen extract, it may appear as a spot of the same colour as the halo.

9.7.3. Structural information

A small amount of information on the chemical structure may be obtained from the position and appearance of the spots on the chromatogram. The colour of the spot bears some relation to chemical structure (Culberson 1972), and the use of MBTH as a visualizing agent gives some additional structural information (see Section 9.5).

9.7.4. Identification of spots

A provisional identification of an unknown spot is achieved by comparison of the characteristics of the spot (R_f, colour, and fluorescence) with published TLC data. Data for many substances have been published by authors including White & James (1985), Culberson & Kristinsson (1970), Culberson (1972), and Culberson *et al.* (1981) (β-orcinol depsidones). Wintabolites (Mietzsch *et al.* 1994) is a Windows application for identification of lichen substances by their TLC (and HPLC) characteristics.

Appendix 1 lists TLC data for 155 commonly occurring lichen substances, including most of the major identified and some major unidentified compunds occurring in British and Irish lichens, together with other compounds which are useful in distinguishing taxa or chemotypes. A larger listing of xanthone data is given in Appendix 2. The R_f values are based mainly on Mietsch *et al.* (1994), but some R_f data (especially solvent system G), and much of the data on colour and fluoresence is based on experimental work by the present authors.

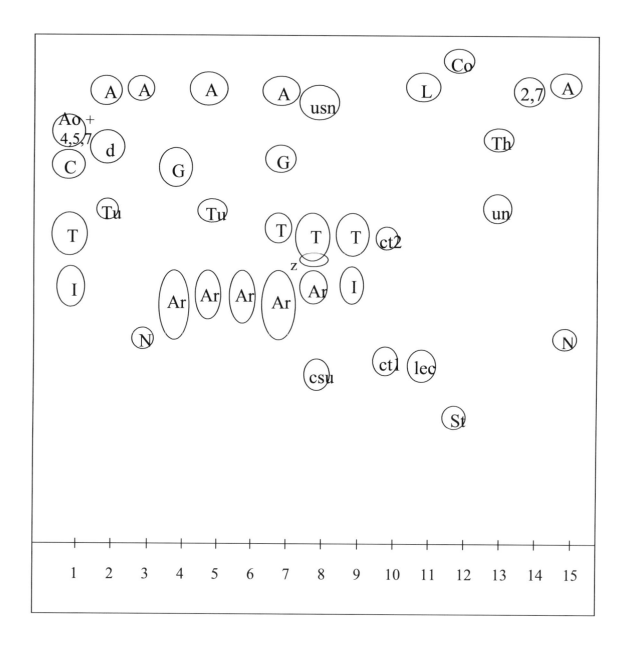

FIG. 11. Chromatogram in Solvent C of some xanthone-containing lichen species (diagrammatic; most minor compounds omitted). Samples are the same as in Fig. 12.

Samples: 1. *Lecidella meiococca*, 2. *Lecidella carpathica*, 3. and 15. controls, 4. *Lecidella elaeochroma* chemotype VI, 5. *Lecidella scabra* chemotype II, 6. *Buellia ocellata*, 7. *Lecanora alboflavida*, 8. *Lecanora expallens*, 9. *Pyrrhospora quernea*, 10. *Lecanora conferta auct. brit.*, 11. *Varicellaria rhodocarpa*, 12. *Pertusaria leioplaca*, 13. *Pertusaria flavida*, 14. *Lecanora albescens*. Abbreviations: A = atranorin, Ao = aotearone, Ar = arthothelin, C = capistratone, Co = coronatone, csu = confusa-unknown, ct1 = conferta-unknown 1, ct2 = conferta-unknown 2, d = diploicin, G = granulosin, I = isoarthothelin, L = lichexanthone, lec = lecanoric acid, N = norstictic acid, St = stictic acid, T = thiophanic acid, Th = thiophaninic acid, Tu = thuringione, un = unknown xanthone, usn = usnic acid, z = zeorin, 2,7 = 2,7-dichlorolichexanthone, 4,5,7 = 4,5,7-trichloro-3-O-methylnorlichexanthone.

66

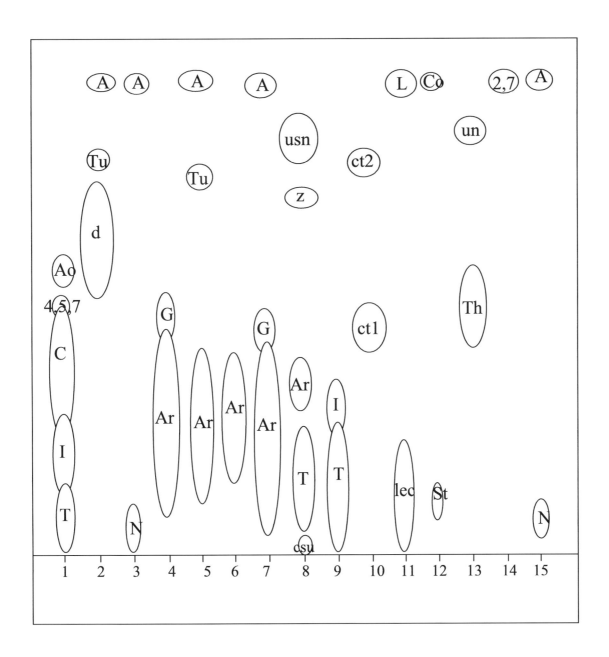

FIG. 12. Chromatogram in Solvent J of some xanthone-containing lichen species (diagrammatic; minor compounds mostly omitted). Samples are the same as in Fig. 11.

Samples: 1. *Lecidella meiococca*, 2. *Lecidella carpathica*, 3. and 15. controls, 4. *Lecidella elaeochroma* chemotype VI, 5. *Lecidella scabra* chemotype II, 6. *Buellia ocellata*, 7. *Lecanora alboflavida*, 8. *Lecanora expallens*, 9. *Pyrrhospora quernea*, 10. *Lecanora conferta auct. brit.*, 11. *Varicellaria rhodocarpa*, 12. *Pertusaria leioplaca*, 13. *Pertusaria flavida*, 14. *Lecanora albescens*. Abbreviations: A = atranorin, Ao = aotearone, Ar = arthothelin, C = capistratone, Co = coronatone, csu = confusa-unknown, ct1 = conferta-unknown 1, ct2 = conferta-unknown 2, d = diploicin, G = granulosin, I = isoarthothelin, L = lichexanthone, lec = lecanoric acid, N = norstictic acid, St = stictic acid, T = thiophanic acid, Th = thiophaninic acid, Tu = thuringione, un = unknown xanthone, usn = usnic acid, z = zeorin, 2,7 = 2,7-dichlorolichexanthone, 4,5,7 = 4,5,7-trichloro-3-O-methylnorlichexanthone.

TABLE 14. Major compounds in selected species of *Lecidella*

Compiled from Leuckert & Knoph (1992), Knoph & Leuckert (1997, 2000) and Tønsberg (1992) and from experimental data. Minor compounds mostly omitted. Roman numerals indicate chemotypes. Note: lichexanthone occurs in addition in sorediate morphs of *L. elaeochroma*. ( ) indicates minor compound.

trivial name	CHEMOTYPE	arthothelin	isoarthothelin	asemone	thiophanic acid	aotearone	thuringione	capistratone	3-O-methylasemone	2,7-dichloro-6-O-methylnorlichexanthone	granulosin	lichexanthone	atranorin	other compounds
position of OCH$_3$		-	-	-	-	3	3	3	3	6	6	3,6		
position of Cl		2,4,5	2,5,7	4,5,7	2,4,5,7	5,7	2,4,5	2,5,7	4,5,7	2,7	2,4,5	-		
L. asema (syn. *L. effugiens*, *L. elaeochromoides*)	I				+								±	
	II			+	+								±	
	III			+	+				+				±	
	IV	+			±								±	
	V	+			±		+						±	
	VI	+			±						+		±	
	VII		+							+				
	VIII		+		+	+			+	(+)			±	
L. carpathica					±								±	diploicin
L. elaeochroma	I		+		+	±		+					±	
	II	+			±								±	
	III	+			±		+						±	
	IV	+			±						+		±	
	V		+								+			
	VI	+										+		
L. flavosorediata		+										+		
L. meiococca			±		+	(+)		+	(+)				±	
L. scabra	I	+											±	
	II	+					+						±	
	III			+									±	
L. stigmataea	I												+	zeorin ±
	II													zeorin ±
	III											+		zeorin
L. subviridis		(+)			+								+	
L. viridans		+			±									
L. wulfenii						+			+				±	

TABLE 15. Major compounds of selected xanthone-containing lichens.

Data compiled from various sources, and from experimental TLC data.

trivial name	arthothelin	isoarthothelin	thiophanic acid	thiophaninic acid	granulosin	lichexanthone	2,7-dichlorolichexanthone	coronatone	conferta-unknowns	confusa-unknown	others
position of OCH3	-	-	-	6	6	3,6	3,6	3,6			
position of Cl	2,4,5	2,5,7	2,4,5,7	2,4	2,4,5	-	2,7	4,5			
Bacidia carneoglauca								±			
Bacidia viridifarinosa								+			zeorin
Buellia ocellata	+										
Lecanora albescens							+				
Lecanora alboflavida	+		+		+						atranorin
Lecanora dispersa							+				
Lecanora andrewii	+										
Lecanora conferta auct. brit.									+		
Lecanora confusa	+[1]		+							+	zeorin, usnic acid
Lecanora expallens	+[1]		+							+	zeorin, usnic acid
Lecanora fugiens	+										
Lecanora pruinosa	+										
Lecanora symmicta	+[1]		+								zeorin, usnic acid
Micarea xanthonica	+[1]		+								
Pertusaria coronata								+			stictic, norstictic ±, constictic ± acids
Pertusaria pertusa								+			constictic and stictic acids
Pertusaria flavicans				+							
Pertusaria flavida				+							
Pertusaria hymenea				+							gyrophoric acid ±
Pertusaria leioplaca								+			stictic ±, norstictic ± and constictic acid ±
Pyrrhospora quernea		+	+								
Varicellaria rhodocarpa						+					lecanoric acid

[1] This compound is similar to arthothelin in Rf, but differs slightly in fluorescence, and may prove to be different.

9.8. Two-dimensional TLC

This method is very valuable where a considerable number of substances are present in a single species, or where there is difficulty in resolving two substances by one-dimensional TLC. It frequently enables identification of accessory substances, and is an important technique for critical investigations. Individual components of closely related groups of substances lying on the same biosynthetic pathway may also be distinguished and identified by this method. Examples include chemosyndromes including stictic, divaricatic, fumarprotocetraric, gyrophoric and perlatolic acids as well as series of triterpenoids. Genera in which two-dimensional TLC is particularly useful include *Pseudocyphellaria*, *Menegazzia* and *Xanthoparmelia*.

In two-dimensional TLC, only one sample is analyzed at a time, together with controls. The plate is run in one solvent, then turned on its side and run in a second solvent. The solvent run in the first system separates the substances as in a one-way chromatogram, but in this instance spreads them as spots along the base line used for the second solvent. These spots are subsequently spread according to their R_f values in the second solvent, resulting in a two-way spread of spots.

The method described below uses part of the plate for one-dimensional runs in the two solvent systems; this serves as a link between the one-way and two-way methods of analysis. In addition, tracings or photocopies of chromatograms can be superimposed so that the positions of control substances (norstictic acid and atranorin) are aligned; in this way the relative positions of unknown spots can be determined, and unknowns can be identified. Identification of unknown substances can thus be ascertained by comparison with the selected one-way controls representing both solvents. Following a two-way analysis of an extract, a useful confirmation of an identification of a substance is to run a second two-way analysis, adding an extract of a known named compound to the starting point, together with the test extract. If the known compound is identical to one in the test extract, the two spots will be superimposed on the two-way chromatogram.

9.8.1. Methods

Solvent systems
In theory any combination of two solvent systems can be used, depending on the nature of the substances being investigated and their respective R_f values. It is important to get the greatest amount of separation with the first solvent system so as to spread the substances well along the axis used for the second separation.

The order of solvents may alter the results slightly. When solvent systems B and C are used together, the use of C as the first solvent is recommended. It is important to dry plates thoroughly between each run; this is easier if the first solvent does not contain acetic or formic acid (e.g. solvent system EH).

Preparation of plates
Normally, 20×20 cm plates are used. Two base lines are drawn 20 mm from the margin of the plate and at right angles to each other as illustrated in Fig. 13. The point where the two lines cross marks the position at which the acetone extract from the lichen to be examined (X) is applied. Three positions, 10 mm apart, are then marked at the far ends of each base line (an additional, outer position is left free here) for additional applications of the extract, and suitable controls, including a mixture of norstictic acid and atranorin. Two finishing lines, at right angles to each other, are drawn 130 mm from each starting line in this example. The layout of the plate can be modified slightly if additional one-directional controls are required, although this subsequently reduces the area available for the two-directional part of the study.

Acetone extracts are carried out as for one-dimensional TLC, and the test extract (X) and suitable controls are spotted along both axes at positions marked C, X and L in Fig. 13, which illustrates the separation of substances related to stictic acid in *Parmotrema perlatum*.

Running and development of the plate
The plate is run in the first solvent system (G in Fig. 13), up to the finishing line for the solvent front. Plates are then air-dried thoroughly, and examined under short wave UV to check that sufficient spreading has occurred along the first axis. The plate is turned through 90°, and run in the second system (A in Fig. 13) up to the second finishing line.

9.8.2. Interpretation of two-dimensional TLC plates

Plates are examined in the same way as in one-dimensional TLC. The substances present in the test sample are resolved as a spread of spots. These may easily be correlated with their one-dimensional positions by a comparison with the controls run in each direction. Often additional spots may be resolved by this method. For further checking or identification a second plate may be run under the same conditions with a mixed extract of the test lichen and a known control (see above).

Artifacts can sometimes be introduced if the compounds decompose before the second solvent is used. Also, the first solvent can alter the properties of the silica gel and thus the R_f values for the second run. Some R_f changes are due to solvent or moisture retained on plate, and vary with drying time.

The positions of spots on two-dimensional chromatograms can provide indications of chemical structure. For instance, series of homologous compounds which differ only in increasing length of carbon side chains lie on straight lines. Using such correlations, tentative identifications of unknown trace compounds can be made; see Culberson & Johnson (1976) for futher details. Two-dimensional chromatograms for some difficult complexes were illustrated by Culberson & Johnson (1976; *Xanthoparmelia loxodes* and *X. verruculifera*), Culberson *et al.* (1981; fumarprotocetraric acid and stictic acid complexes, and the compounds of *Xanthoparmelia quintaria*), and Wilkins & James (1979; compounds in *Pseudocyphellaria*).

9.9. Preparative thin-layer chromatography

Lichen substances which have separated from each other on a TLC plate (which has not yet been treated with visualizing agents) can be extracted from the plate and used for further analyses. This is necessary if a relatively pure sample of the substance is required rather than a mixture of substances, for instance for microcrystal tests, spot tests, microhydrolysis, or as a control in further TLC runs.

It is necessary to use a relatively large amount of lichen (for instance at least 5-10 times the usual amount for TLC), to make up for losses during extraction. The lichen extract is applied as a band along the starting line of the plate, rather than as spots. The developed plate is examined under short-wave ultra-violet, and the dark band corresponding to the chemical required is indicated by a pencil line. The position of fatty acids must be established by spraying the plate with water. The silica gel layer is scraped from the plate, and extracted with acetone in a test tube (or in suitable preparative glassware).

Special preparative TLC plates have a thicker than usual layer of silica gel for extraction of larger quantities of substances. If the plate does not contain a fluorescent indicator, the position of the required chemical must be found by other means, for instance removing part of the plate and visualizing the spots by sulphuric acid and heat, and comparing the position on the treated and untreated plates.

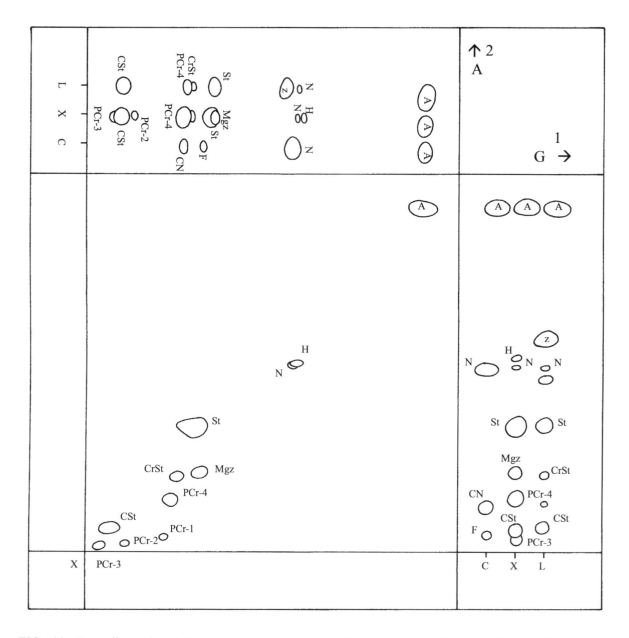

FIG. 13. Two-dimensional G × A chromatogram of *Parmotrema perlatum* with one-dimensional comparisons. Samples: X = *Parmotrema perlatum*, C = control mixture of *Cladonia subcervicornis* and *Pleurosticta acetabulum*, L = *Lepraria lobificans*. Compounds: A = atranorin, CN = connorstictic acid, CrSt = cryptostictic acid, CSt = constictic acid, F = fumarprotocetraric acid, H = hypostictic acid, Mgz = menegazziaic acid, N = norstictic acid; Pcr-1, Pcr-2, Pcr-3 and Pcr-4 are unidentified compounds (Culberson *et al.* 1981).

9.10. Microhydrolysis

Lichen depsides comprise two or more carbon rings joined by an ester linkage (–COO–) which is easily hydrolyzed, resulting in cleavage of the original molecule into two or more entities (Fig. 14). These cleavage products can be analyzed by TLC in the usual way. This method has been used primarily for investigations of the structure of unknown substances (e.g. Culberson & Culberson 1966), but also allows separation of compounds which are otherwise difficult to separate due to similar R_f values, such as the depsides imbricaric acid and stenosporic acid, and perlatolic acid and sphaerophorin (Fig. 15).

The following procedure for acid hydrolysis follows Culberson (1972), who also lists R_f data for 37 hydrolysis products of depsides:

1. Dissolve samples of 0.1–0.3 mg of pure compound or crude lichen extract in concentrated sulphuric acid (3-6 drops) in a vial.
2. Cool in a freezer for 15–30 minutes.
3. Add crushed ice to the vial to dilute the sulphuric acid.
4. Extract hydrolysis products with diethyl ether: add a small amount of ether to the vial and shake; draw off the floating layer of ether with a pipette and evaporate on a microscope slide; repeat two or more times.
5. Chromatograph the residue on the slide in 3 solvent systems, together with crude unhydrolyzed extract.

If the compound of interest occurs in the lichen with other hydrolyzable compounds, they must first be separated by preparative TLC. When two compounds are to be distinguished by microhydrolysis, the original compounds and the cleavage products of both should be compared on the same TLC plates.

Hydrolysis can also be acheived with 5% KOH at 100°C for 30–60 minutes, when the products lack the carboxyl (–COOH) group. It is not necessary to rely solely on published TLC data for cleavage products. The cleavage products of a depside can be predicted from its structure, so that the hydrolysis products of depsides of known structure can be used as controls. For instance, the structure in the bottom left of Fig. 14 would also be expected as a product of hydrolysis of imbricaric acid, and the structure at bottom right would be expected from the hydrolysis of glomelliferic or olivetoric acid.

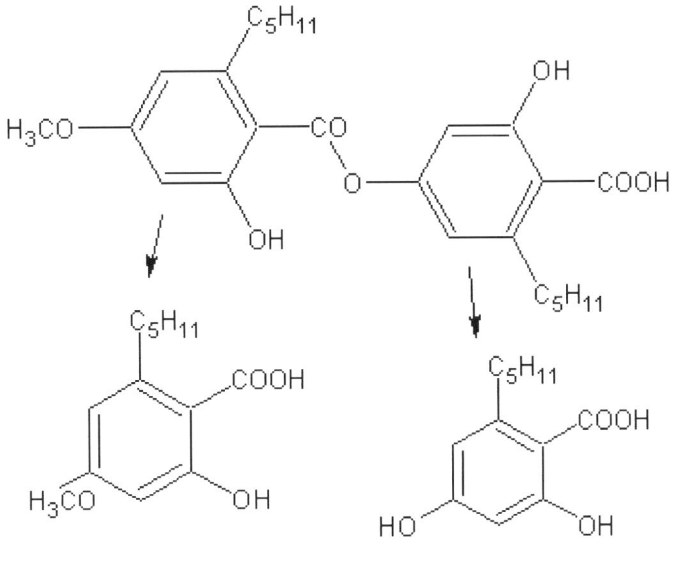

FIG. 14. Perlatolic acid (top; a *para*-depside), and the two products obtained by microhydrolysis with sulphuric acid: 2-hydroxy-4-methoxy-6-n-pentylbenzoic acid (bottom left) and 2,4-dihydroxy-6-n-pentylbenzoic acid (bottom right).

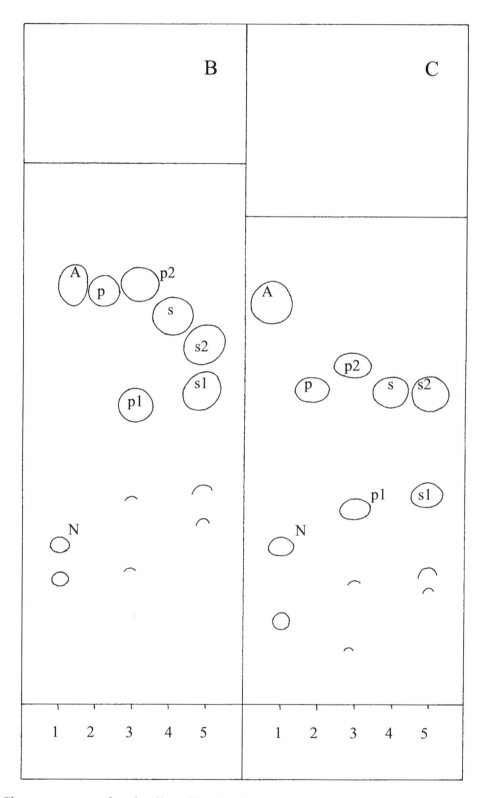

FIG. 15. Chromatograms of perlatolic acid and sphaerophorin and their acid hydrolysis products in solvent systems B and C.

Samples: 1. controls, 2. perlatolic acid, 3. hydrolysis products of perlatolic acid, 4. sphaerophorin, 5. hydrolysis products of sphaerophorin. A = atranorin, N = norstictic acid, p = perlatolic acid, p1 = 2,4-dihydroxy-6-n-pentylbenzoic acid, p2 = 2-hydroxy-4-methoxy-6-n-pentylbenzoic acid, s = sphaerophorin, s1 = 2,4-dihydroxy-6-n-heptylbenzoic acid, s2 = 2-hydroxy-4-methoxy-6-methylbenzoic acid. Arcs indicate trace amounts of other substances.

9.11. High Performance Thin-layer Chromatography (HPTLC)

HPTLC is a technique which works on the same principles as TLC. However, the plates are coated with a finer-grained silica gel, allowing greater resolution of spots. The standard plates are smaller than TLC plates, typically 10 × 10 cm or smaller, and must be dried at 50° C after application of the samples. Samples are applied using 1 μl capillary tubes, preferably using a device to assist in accurate placement. The plate is developed horizontally within a small enclosed chamber, using only a few ml of solvent. The advantages of HPTLC over TLC are said to be greater resolution of spots, greater sensitivity, greater speed, and smaller consumption of solvents. Samples may be applied at both sides of a 10 × 10 cm plate, and developed towards the centre of the plate, so that 38 samples can be run on a single plate. Thus, the cost per sample is less, approximately 10.6-12.0 p per sample at current prices for HPTLC, compared to approximately 15.4 p per sample using glass TLC plates. The different properties of plates used in TLC and HPTLC mean that chromatographic data of substances may differ between the two methods. Full details of the technique, and data for 69 compounds, are provided by Arup *et al.* (1993). Critics of the technique find the small plates used in HPTLC difficult to analyze.

10. EQUIPMENT AND SUPPLIERS

10.1 Equipment checklist for TLC

TLC plates: for general purposes, use plates which contain a substance which fluoresces under short wave UV ('F$_{254}$'). Aluminium plates are cheaper than glass, and can be cut with a knife, but they are not suitable for detecting fatty acids. Merck silica gel 60 F$_{254}$ pre-coated 20 × 20 cm plates are used as a standard by many workers. These cost £178 for a pack of 25 plates in 2009 (equivalent to 37.5 p per sample) (Sigma-Aldrich catalogue number Z293024). (Preparative TLC plates have a thicker layer of silica gel, and are used when substances are to be separated and then extracted from the plate for further analysis, but they are not used for routine analysis).

TLC developing tanks: these vary in cost and complexity; some have internal gutters to hold solvent, or grooves for glass rods to hold TLC plates upright, so that two or more plates can be developed at once. The base of the tank may be flat or shallowly V-shaped. The lid should be closely fitting. TLC tanks with two troughs in the base can also be used for pre-equilibration of plates: the solution for pre-equilibration (e.g. acetic acid) is placed in one trough, and the TLC plate placed in the adjacent dry trough. A simple design of tank is adequate for TLC, but rectangular glass jars with an uneven base are not suitable. It is useful to own more than one tank so that several solvents can be in use at once. A tank of simple design was offered for £64.40 in 2009 by Sigma-Aldrich (catalogue number Z126195).

UV lamp: a hand-held mains operated combined short wave (254 nm) and long wave (365 nm) lamp is suitable.

Ultra-violet protective spectacles or face shield. These must be specifically designed to protect from UV radiation.

Spray or brush for application of sulphuric acid.

Spray for water: a plastic, hand-pumped spray is suitable.

Microcentrifuge tubes, Eppendorf type, polypropylene tubes with integral cap. A size of 30 × 8 mm, capacity 0.5 ml, is adequate for normal purposes. Lichen samples can be extracted in these, and the sealed tube can be stored inside the herbarium packet and used for a second extraction if necessary. A carefully extracted lichen fragment also retains its morphological features and can be re-examined.

Capillary tubes: disposable capillary tubes 65-90 mm long, with an internal diameter of 0.6 mm are suitable. Tubes with too large an internal diameter create too large a spot. Custom-made tubes (see Bilbate in Section 10.3) are adequate; Drummond Microcaps 20μl capacity are suitable but more expensive.

Silicone grease for sealing lid of developing tank.

10 % H$_2$SO$_4$.

Acetone.
Solvents (see Section 9.2).
Oven (to develop plates at 110°C).

10.2. Other equipment

Battery operated long-wave UV lamps: these can often be obtained from suppliers of philately materials. The JML 1197UV Super Mini Ultra Violet Fluorescent Lantern performs well. Camag horizontal developing chamber for HPTLC, for 10 × 10 cm plate. This was recommended by Arup *et al.* (1993). Offered for £693 by Labpak (2009).

10. 3. Suppliers of equipment and chemicals

Solvents, general chemicals and general laboratory equipment (such as test tubes) can be obtained from any chemical supply company, although most of these are reluctant to supply individuals. Some more specialized U.K. suppliers are:

Sigma-Aldrich, The Old Brickyard, New Road, Gillingham, Dorset, SP8 4XT. www.sigmaaldrich.com. Tel. 0800 717181. Supply Merck TLC plates, developing tanks, UV lamps, microcentrifuge tubes, microcapillary tubes and general and specialized chemicals.

P & R Labpak Limited, Unit 6, Ketterer Court, Jackson Street, St. Helens, Merseyside, WA9 3AH. Tel. 0870 034 2055. www.prlabs.co.uk. Supply Merck TLC and HPTLC plates, Camag horizontal developing chambers for HPTLC, a TLC/HPTLC plate cutter, and UV lamps

Bilbate Limited, 24 High March, Daventry, Northamptonshire NN11 4HB. www.bilbate.co.uk. Tel. 01327 705113. An inexpensive source of custom-made capillary tubes; 1.00 mm × 0.6 mm internal diameter × 90 mm are suitable.

11. HEALTH AND SAFETY

The information given below and in Appendix 3 is intended only as a brief introduction for those persons considering acquiring and using the chemicals mentioned in this book. Before acquiring and using any of these chemicals, the user must obtain, read and understand the safety data produced by the chemical supplier, and any other data relevant to the safe storage, handling and disposal of the chemicals.

11.1. Introduction

The potential user of any of the chemicals mentioned in this book must become familiar with the hazards associated with each chemical before it is acquired or used. The user must also be aware of precautions to be taken to minimize the risks associated with the use of the chemical, and procedures to be taken in case of accidents. Copies of relevant data should be stored near to the working area. The user should prepare a summary sheet for each chemical and how it will be used (a COSHH form and risk assesment in the U.K.), giving details of risks, safety precautions, first aid, how to deal with spillages, and methods for disposal. The equipment needed for safe use of the chemicals should be available before the chemical is acquired. For any procedure, one should always look for less hazardous methods of achieving the same result.

11.2. Hazards and risk assessment

The hazards associated with each chemical must be understood by the user before the chemical is acquired or used. Suppliers of dangerous chemicals are required to classify each chemical according to one of a number of categories of danger, and to provide the recipient of the chemical with a safety data sheet which describes the hazards associated with the chemical, and the precautions to be taken. The hazards and precautions may be described by allocation of one or more standard risk phrases and safety phrases. Information on hazards can also be found in publications such as Health and Safety Executive (2000), Kellard (1986, and later amendments) and Luxon (1992). Some commercial catalogues also list risk and safety phrases. Note that new information on the hazards of a substance may be appear at any time.

The hazards of each chemical mentioned in this book are summarized in Appendix 3, but reading this appendix is not a substitute for acquiring full hazard and safety data. Note that the absence of a particular risk or safety phrase for a chemical does not mean that it is harmless in this respect.

The potential user of dangerous chemicals must assess the risks associated with any procedure using these chemicals, and decide what precautions are needed to prevent or adequately control exposure, and inform any other people who are involved; this is a legal requirement for employers in the U.K. under the Control of Substances Hazardous to Health Regulations 1999, commonly known as COSHH (Health and Safety Executive 1999a). When a risk assessment is carried out, consider the hazards associated with the substances, the likely route of entry into the body (inhalation, ingestion, or through the skin), the concentration or conditions which may cause ill-health, the quantity of the chemical in use, the volatility or dustiness of the chemical, and the precautions necessary for safe use during the whole procedure, including disposal.

Appendix 3 assigns each chemical to an overall hazard group, based on the risk phrases associated with the chemical, following Health and Safety Executive (1999b). Hazard groups A-E comprise chemicals causing harm when inhaled, with A the least hazardous, D the more hazardous, and E comprising special cases of hazardous chemicals. S indicates chemicals causing harm in contact with skin and eyes. Briefly, the categories A-E correspond to chemicals known to have or suspected to have the following types of hazard:

Category E: causing cancer, mutation, heritable genetic damage or sensitization.
Category D: very toxic, toxic and causing serious damage by long-term exposure, irreversible effects, damage to the unborn child, impaired fertility.
Category C: toxic, causing burns or severe burns, irritating to skin or respiratory system, risk of serious damage to the eyes, harmful with risk of irreversible effects or serious damage to health by prolonged exposure.
Category B: chemicals classified as harmful but not causing irreversible effects.
Category A: chemicals classified as irritants, or chemicals of low hazard.

Note that these categories apply only to health hazards, and do not take account of additional hazards such as extreme flammability. For chemicals in categories D and E, the user should decide whether the chemical is really necessary, and whether there may be a less hazardous alternative. If the chemical is used, specialist advice must be sought on safety. Before any chemical is acquired, the potential user must decide whether he or she has the necessary experience and facilities to store, use and dispose of the chemical in a safe manner.

The potential user should be aware of risks associated with reactions between chemicals, which may be violent or release toxic vapours. For instance, nitric acid is incompatible in this respect with acetic acid, acetone, and other flammable liquids, and iodine is incompatible with ammonia solution. Concentrated sulphuric acid reacts violently with water, and when preparing a 10% solution of sulphuric acid, the acid must be added carefully to the water, not the other way round.

11.3. Storage
All hazardous substances must be stored in a clean, dry, cool, tidy and secure place. Volatile materials must be stored in a well-ventilated area. Frequently used solvents may be stored in small quantities in

a specially designed metal cabinet; larger quantities and infrequently used solvents should be in a properly constructed fireproof store. Incompatible materials (such as flammable substances and oxidizing agents) must not be stored near to each other.

11.4. Handling

All volatile and dusty substances must be handled in a fume cupboard. If a fume cupboard vented to the outside is not available, portable fume cupboards which rely on disposable charcoal filters can be used. The performance of the filter must be checked regularly; check also that the type of filter is suitable for all the substances to be used.

Personal protective equipment should be used where indicated by the safety phrases quoted in the supplier's safety data. When choosing equipment, specialist advice should be sought to ensure that the equipment is appropriate for the chemical and process in use. Full-face shields are appropriate for handling corrosive liquids. If protective gloves are used, it is essential to choose the correct type; contact the glove manufacturers for details. For instance, nitrile gloves are recommended for many solvents, but are not suitable for dioxane. Even some recommended gloves may be penetrated by some solvents mentioned in this book in as little as 5 minutes, which suggests they are probably not suitable in this case. Heavy duty neoprene gloves are good for general use and can be reused, but in general it is probably safer, although more expensive, to use disposable protective equipment. Take care that contamination does not occur as gloves are removed, and dispose of used gloves sensibly.

Ingestion of chemicals is unlikely to occur if hands are washed after handling chemicals. Mouth pipettes should never be used to transfer liquids.

11.5. Spillages

Accidental spillages may occur even when chemicals are stored and handled carefully. It is essential that the user should know in advance how to deal with spillages of chemicals that are currently in use, and have the necessary equipment to hand. The type of spill which should be prepared for will be clear from the type and quantity of chemicals in use, and the procedures in which they are used. For instance, the use of chemicals in TLC could result in the breakage of a 1 litre bottle of toluene during preparation of a solvent system.

When a spill occurs, the user must decide whether the spill can be contained by him or her, or whether more specialist help is required. Unless the spill is very small and of low hazard, persons working nearby should be informed and steps taken to contain the spill. For volatile materials, sources of ignition must be isolated. Flammable vapour may travel considerable distances from the site of the spill, and flash-back from sources of ignition. The user should be familiar with emergency procedures in force within the building, and with the location and method of use of emergency spillage and fire-fighting equipment.

Spills are often dealt with by absorbing the spill onto a solid material, after which it can be collected and neutralized, removed to a safe area for evapouration, or disposed of. Warren (1993, and later amendments) presents general procedures for dealing with groups of chemicals, such as inorganic acids, or hydrocarbons. The necessary materials for absorption and containment should be available near to the working area. As well as substances recommended for specific groups of chemicals, commercially available inert fabrics and absorbent particulate material may be useful. Universal spill kits may be considered, containing absorbents, protective items such as gloves and goggles, and a sealable drum.

11.6. First aid

If a person is accidentally exposed to a hazardous chemical, assistance should be sought immediately from a qualified first aider, and professional medical help should be obtained. For some types of exposure, such as contact of hazardous chemicals with the eyes, immediate assistance from a bystander is vital to minimize damage. Information on first aid in relation to chemical hazards can be found in Luxon (1992) and Volans (1994, and later amendments).

The user of hazardous chemicals should know the identity of the relevant safety officer and first aider in a building, the location of the nearest first aid box, and the telephone number of the nearest casualty department.

12.7. Disposal

Hazardous waste chemicals should be stored safely until disposal by a licensed disposal company. Waste chlorinated solvents (chloroform and dichloromethane) should be collected separately from non-chlorinated. All waste material must be correctly labelled. It may be possible to dispose of small (for instance <50 ml) quantities of substances miscible with water and of low hazard by washing them into drains with copious amounts of water (at least 1000 times the volume of the substance is recommmended), but it is essential to check the relevant regulations first (in the U.K. the Environment Agency must be contacted before disposal into drains).

12. REFERENCES

Ahmadjian, V. & Hale, M.E. (1973) *The Lichens*. New York and London: Academic Press.

Aptroot, A., Thor, G., Lücking, R., Elix, J.A. & Chaves, J.L. (2009) The lichen genus *Herpothallon* reinstated. *Bibliotheca Lichenologica* **99**: 19-66.

Archer, A.W. (1978) 3-Methyl-2-benzothiazolone hydrazone hydrochloride as a spray reagent for phenolic lichen compounds. *Journal of Chromatography* **152**: 290-292.

Archer, A. (1984) Detection of didymic acid. *British Lichen Society Bulletin* **54**: 23-24.

Archer (1993) Identification of orcinol *para*-depsides in the lichen genus *Pertusaria* by thin-layer chromatography. *Mycotaxon* **46**: 1-4.

Arup, U., Ekman, S., Lindblom, L. & Mattson, J.-E. (1993) High performance thin layer chromatography (HPTLC), an improved technique for screening lichen substances. *Lichenologist* **25**: 61-71.

Asahina, (1939) Mikrochemischer Nachweis der Flechtenstoff (X). *Journal of Japanese Botany* **15**: 465-472.

Baral, H.O. (1987) Lugol's Solution/IKI versus Melzer's reagent: Hemiamyloidity, a universal feature of the ascus wall. *Mycotaxon* **29**: 399-450.

Baral, H.O. (1992) Vital versus herbarium taxonomy: morphological differences between living and dead cells of Ascomycetes, and their taxonomic implications. *Mycotaxon* **54**: 333-390.

Beaver, P. (1992) Precautions against radiation. In *Hazards in the Chemical Laboratory*. 5th Edn. (S.G. Luxon, ed): 123-140. Cambridge: The Royal Chemical Society.

Brodo, I.M. (1986) Interpreting chemical variation in lichens for systematic purposes. *Bryologist* **89**: 132-138.

Brodo, I.M. & Hawksworth, D.L. (1977) *Alectoria* and allied genera in North America. *Opera Botanica* **42**: 1-164.

Bungartz, F. & Wirth, V. (2007) *Buellia peregrina* sp. nov., a new, euendolithic calcicolous lichen species from the Namib Desert. *Lichenologist* **39**: 41-45.

Common, R.S. (1991) The distribution and taxonomic significance of lichenan and isolichenan in the Parmeliaceae (Lichenized Ascomycotina), as determined by iodine reactions. I. Introduction and Methods. II. The genus *Alectoria* and associated taxa. *Mycotaxon* **41**: 67-112.

Common, R.S. & Brodo, I.M. (1995) *Bryoria* Sect. *Subdivergentes* recognized as the new genus *Nodobryoria* (Lichenized Ascomycotina). *Bryologist* **98**: 189-206.

Culberson, C.F. (1969) *Chemical and Botanical Guide to Lichen Products*. Chapel Hill: The University of North Carolina Press.

Culberson, C.F. (1970) Supplement to 'Chemical and Botanical Guide to Lichen Products'. *Bryologist* **73:** 177-377.

Culberson, C.F. (1972) Improved conditions and new data for the identification of lichen products by a standardized thin-layer chromatographic method. *Journal of Chromatography* **72:** 113-125.

Culberson, C.F. (1974) Conditions for the use of Merck silica gel 60 F254 plates in the standardized thin-layer chromatographic technique for lichen products. *Journal of Chromatography* **97:** 107-108.

Culberson, C.F. & Ammann, K. (1979) Standardmethode zur Dünnschichtchromatographie von Flechtensubstanzen. *Herzogia* **5:** 1-24.

Culberson, C.F. & Culberson, W.L. (1966) The identification of imbricaric acid and a new imbricaric acid-containing lichen species. *Bryologist* **69:** 192-202.

Culberson, C.F. & Elix, J.A. (1989) Lichen Substances. *In Methods in Plant Biochemistry. Vol. 1. Plant Phenolics* (J.B. Harborne, ed): 509-535.

Culberson, C.F., Culberson, W.L. & Johnson, A. (1977) *Second Supplement to 'Chemical and Botanical Guide to Lichen Products'*. St. Louis: The American Bryological and Lichenological Society.

Culberson, C.F., Culberson, W.L. & Johnson, A. (1981) A standardized TLC analysis of β-orcinol depsidones. *Bryologist* **84:** 16-29.

Culberson, C.F. & Johnson, A. (1976) A standardized two-dimensional thin-layer chromatographic method for lichen products. *Journal of Chromatography* **128:** 253-259.

Culberson, C.F. & Johnson, A. (1982) Substitution of methyl *tert.*-butyl ether for diethyl ether in the standardized thin-layer chromatographic method for lichen products. *Journal of Chromatography* **238:** 483-487.

Culberson, C.F. & Kristinsson, H. (1969) A standardized method for the identification of lichen products. *Journal of Chromatography* **46:** 85-93.

Degelius, G. (1954) The lichen genus *Collema* in Europe. Morphology, taxonomy, ecology. *Symbolae Botanicae Upsalienses* **13:** 1-499.

Dobson, F.S. (2001) The problems and dangers of using para-phenylenediamine. *British Lichen Society Bulletin* **88:** 56-57.

Dobson, F.S. (2004) More thoughts on spot tests. *British Lichen Society Bulletin* **94:** 65-67.

Egan, R.S. (1986) Correlations and non-correlations of chemical variation patterns with lichen morphology and geography. *Bryologist* **89:** 99-110.

Egan, R.S. (2001) Long-term storage of TLC data. *Evansia* **18:** 19-20.

Elix, J.A. (1993) Progress in the generic delimitation of *Parmelia sensu lato* Lichens (Ascomycotina: Parmeliaceae) and a synoptic key to the Parmeliaceae. *Bryologist* **96:** 359-383.

Elix, J.A. & Stocker-Wörgötter, E.(2008) Biochemistry and Secondary Metabolites. In *Lichen Biology* (T.H. Nash, ed): 104-133. Cambridge: Cambridge University Press.

Elix, J.A. & Crook, C.E. (1992) The joint occurrences of chloroxanthones in lichens, and a further thirteen new lichen xanthones. *Bryologist* **95:** 52-64.

Elix, J.A., Whitton, A.A. & Sargent, M.V. (1984) Recent progress in the chemistry of lichen substances. *Fortschritte der Chemie organischer Naturstoffe* **45:** 103-234.

Fryday, A.M. (1992a) A microscopic test for confluentic acid. *British Lichen Society Bulletin* **70:** 31.

Fryday, A.M. (1992b) The chemistry of the new confluentic acid test. *British Lichen Society Bulletin* **71:** 41.

Fryday, A.M. (2002) A revision of the species of the *Rhizocarpon hochstetterri* group occurring in the British Isles. *Lichenologist* **34:** 451-477.

Gahan, P.B. (1984) *Plant Histochemistry and Cytochemistry. An Introduction*. London: Academic Press.

Grube, M. (1993) Über metachromatisches Färbeverhalten bei einigen Arten der Sammelgattung *Arthopyrenia*, mit weiteren Beispielen aus ähnlichen Gattungen (Ascomycetes, Arthopyreniaceae). *Nova Hedwigia* **57:** 473-482.

Hafellner, J. & Kalb, K. (1995) Studies in Trichotheliales *ordo novus*. In *Studies in Lichenology with Emphasis on Chemotaxonomy, Geography and Phytochemistry, Festschrift Ch. Leuckert* (J.-G. Knoph, K. Schrüfer & H.J.M. Sipman, eds), *Bibliotheca Lichenologica* **57**: 161-186.

Hale, M.E. (1983) *The Biology of Lichens*. 3rd edition. London: Arnold.

Hanko, B. (1983) Die Chemotypen der Flechtengattung *Pertusaria* in Europa. *Bibliotheca Lichenologica* **19**: 1-296.

Hawksworth, D.L. (1976) Lichen Chemotaxonomy. In *Lichenology: Progress and Problems* (D.H. Brown, D.L. Hawksworth & R.H. Bailey, eds): 139-184. London: Academic Press.

Hawksworth, D.L. & Hill, D.J. (1984) *The Lichen-forming Fungi*. Glasgow and London: Blackie.

Hawksworth, D.L., Kirk, P.M., Sutton, B.C. & Pegler, D.N. (1995) *Dictionary of the Fungi*. 8th Edn. Wallingford: CAB International.

Health and Safety Executive (1999a) *The Control of Substances Hazardous to Health Regulations 1999*. London: Stationery Office.

Health and Safety Executive (1999b) *COSHH Essentials. Easy Steps to Control Chemicals*. Sudbury: HSE Books.

Health and Safety Executive (2000) *Approved Supply List*. 6th Edn. Sudbury: HSE Books.

Holtan-Hartwig, J. (1993) The lichen genus *Peltigera*, exclusive of the *P. canina* group, in Norway. *Sommerfeltia* **15**: 1-77.

Huneck, S. (1973) Nature of Lichen Substances. In *The Lichens* (V. Ahmadjian & M.E. Hale, eds): 495-522.

Huneck, S. (1984) Fortschritte der Chemie von Flechtenstoffe. *Beiheft zur Nova Hedwigia* **79**: 793-838.

Huneck, S. & Yoshimura, I. (1996) *Identification of Lichen Substances*. Berlin: Springer-Verlag.

James, P.W. & White, F.J. (1987) Studies on the genus *Nephroma* I. The European and Macaronesian species. *Lichenologist* **19**: 215-268.

Kellard, B. (ed) (1986, with later amendments) *Croner's Substances Hazardous to Health*. Kingston upon Thames: Croner.CCH Group Ltd.

Kirschbaum, U. & Wirth, V. (1995) *Flechten erkennen – Luftgüte bestimmen*. Stuttgart: Ulmer.

Knoph, J.G. & Leuckert, C. (1997) Chemotypes and distribution patterns of the non-saxicolous species of *Lecidella* (Lecanoraceae, Lecanorales). *Bibliotheca Lichenologica* **68**: 129-134.

Knoph, J.G. & Leuckert, C. (2000) Chemotaxonomische Studien in der Gattung *Lecidella* (Lecanorales, Lecanoraceae) III. Die gesteinsbewohnenden Arten mit farblosem Hypothecium unter besonderer Berücksichtigung von europäischem Material. *Herzogia* **14**: 1-26.

Leuckert, C. & Knoph, J.-G. (1992) European taxa of saxicolous *Lecidella* containing chloroxanthones: identification of patterns using thin layer chromatography. *Lichenologist* **24**: 383-397.

Luxon, S.G. (1992) *Hazards in the Chemical Laboratory*. 5th Edn. Cambridge: The Royal Chemical Society.

Melzer, V. (1924) L'ornementation des spores des Russules. *Bulletin Trimestriel de la Société Mycologique de France* **40**: 78-81.

Meyer, B. & Printzen, C. (2000) Proposal for a standardized nomenclature and characterization of insoluble lichen pigments. *Lichenologist* **32**: 571-583.

Mietzsch, E. , Lumbsch, H.T. & Elix, J.A. (1994) *Wintabolites (Mactabolites for Windows) Users Manual*. 2nd Edn. Essen: Universität Essen.

Mosbach, K. (1973) Biosynthesis of lichen substances. In *The Lichens* (V. Ahmadjian & M.E. Hale, eds): 523-546. London and New York: Academic Press.

Nash III, T.H., Hafellner, J. & Common, R.S. (1990) *Omphalora*, a new genus in the Parmeliaceae. *Lichenologist* **22**: 355-365.

Orange, A. (1992) A key to the *Cladonia chlorophaea* group in Europe, using microcrystal tests. *British Lichen Society Bulletin* **70**: 36-42.

Poelt, J. & Leuckert, C. (1993) Substitution and supplementary addition of secondary products in the evolution of lichenized Ascomycotina. In *Phytochemistry and Chemotaxonomy of Lichenized Ascomycetes – A Festschrift in honour of Siegfried Huneck* (G.B. Feige & H.T. Lumbsch, eds), *Bibliotheca Lichenologica* **53**: 201-215.

Printzen, C. & Tønsberg, T. (2003) Four new species and three new apothecial pigments of *Biatora*. In *Lichenological Contributions in Honour of G.B. Feige* (M. Jensen, ed), *Bibliotheca Lichenologica* **86**: 133-145.

Purvis, O.W., Elix, J.A., Broomhead, J.A. & Jones, G.C. (1987) The occurrence of copper-norstictic acid in lichens from cupriferous substrata. *Lichenologist* **19**: 193-203.

Rogers, R.W. (1989) Chemical variation and the species concept in lichenized fungi. *Botanical Journal of the Linnean Society* **101**: 229-239.

Roux, C. & Triebel, D. (1994) Révision des espèces de *Stigmidium* et de *Sphaerellothecium* (champignons lichénicoles non lichénisés, Ascomycetes) correspondant à *Pharcidia epicymatia* sensu Keissler ou à *Stigmidium schaereri* auct. *Bulletin de la Société Linnéenne de Provence* **45**: 451-542.

Roux, C., Triebel, D., Bricaud, O. & Le Coeur, D. (1995) Le *Stigmidium lecidellae* sp. nov. et remarques sur le genre *Stigmidium* (champignons lichénicoles non lichénisée, Ascomycètes) *Canadian Journal of Botany* **73**: 662-672.

Santesson, J. (1967) Chemical studies on lichens 4. Thin layer chromatography of lichen substances. *Acta Chemica Scandinavica* **21**: 1162-1172.

Santesson, J. (1968) Chemical studies on lichens 13. A spot test for lichen xanthones. *Acta Chemica Scandinavica* **22**: 2398.

Smith, C.W., Aptroot, A., Coppins, B.J., Fletcher, A., Gilbert, O.L., James, P.W. & Wolseley, P.A. (2009) *The Lichens of Great Britain and Ireland*. London: British Lichen Society.

Thomson, J.W. (1967) *The Lichen Genus* Cladonia *in North America*. Toronto: University of Toronto Press.

Timdal, E. (1984) The delimitation of *Psora* (Lecideaceae) and related genera, with notes on some species. *Nordic Journal of Botany* **4**: 525-540.

Tønsberg, T. (1992) The sorediate and isidiate, corticolous, crustose lichens in Norway. *Sommerfeltia* **14**: 1-331.

Volans, G. (ed) (1994, and amendments to 2000) *Substances Hazardous to Health. Emergency First Aid Guide*. Kingston upon Thames: Croner.CCH Group Ltd.

Walker, F.J. & James, P.W. (1980) A revised guide to microchemical techniques for the identification of lichen products. *British Lichen Society Bulletin* **46**: 13-29 (supplement).

Warren, P.J. (ed) (1993, and amendments to 2000) *Substances Hazardous to Health. Emergency Spillage Guide*. Kingston upon Thames: Croner.CCH Group Ltd.

White, F.W. & James, P.W. (1985) A new guide to microchemical techniques for the identification of lichen substances. *British Lichen Society Bulletin* **57** (supplement).

White, F.J. & James, P.W. (1986) A chemical checklist of British lichens: part 1. *British Lichen Society Bulletin* **58**: 40-48.

White, F.J. & James, P.W. (1987) A chemical checklist of British lichens: part 2. *British Lichen Society Bulletin* **60**: 42-47, figure.

Wilkins, A.L. & James, P.W. (1979) The chemistry of *Pseudocyphellaria impressa* s. lat. in New Zealand. *Lichenologist* **11**: 271-281.

Yasue, T. (1969) Histochemical identification of calcium oxalate. *Acta Histochemica et Cytochemica* **2**: 83-95.

Appendix 1. TLC data for commonly encountered lichen substances

With few exceptions, relative Rf in solvents A, B & C follows Wintabolites (Mietzsch *et al.* 1994); Rf in solvent G partly follows Wintabolites, and is partly based on experimental data. Spot colour and UV fluorescence based largely on White & James (1985) and experimental data. Substances listed in order of relative Rf in solvent C.

COMPOUND	RELATIVE Rf				UV BEFORE HEATING	SPOT COLOUR AFTER ACID AND HEATING	UV AFTER HEATING	SUGGESTED CONTROL SPECIES	NOTES
	C	A	B	G					
erythrin	1	4	2	11	-	yellow to orange	dark green	Dirina massiliensis	orcinol *para*-despide
PCr-3		2		8	-	orange	-	Parmotrema crinitum, P. perlatum (traces)	β-orcinol depsidone; part of stictic acid chemosyndrome, use 2-way TLC
constictic acid	2	7	1	9	-	brownish orange, or pinkish orange, turning brownish 24 hrs	-	Xanthoparmelia conspersa, Parmotrema crinitum, P. perlatum, Menegazzia terebrata	β-orcinol depsidone; part of stictic acid chemosyndrome
PCr-2		2		13	-	grey	-	Parmotrema crinitum, P. perlatum (traces)	β-orcinol depsidone; part of stictic acid chemosyndrome, use 2-way TLC
confumarprotocetraric acid	2	2	2	15	faint + orange	pale orange	-	Cladonia ciliata (trace)	β-orcinol depsidone; minor compound often found with fumarprotocetraric acid
4-oxypannaric acid 2-methyl ester	3	15		23	-	pale lilac-grey	-	Lepraria diffusa (major)	dibenzofurane; very pale brownish on plate before heating
connorstictic acid	3	11	11	26	-	orange	-	Pleurosticta acetabulum, Phlyctis argena (minor in both)	β-orcinol depsidone; occurs with norstictic acid
rhodocladonic acid	4	0	1		dark purple	dull red-purple	-	Cladonia floerkeana (and other red-fruited spp.)	naphthaquinone; red pigment in apothecia
salazinic acid	4	10	7	26	-	orange	-	Parmelia sulcata	β-orcinol depsidone
PCr-4		13		26	-	yellow-orange	-	Parmotrema crinitum, P. perlatum	β-orcinol depsidone; part of stictic acid chemosyndrome, separate from cryptostictic acid in A, or use 2-way TLC
siphulin	4	14		37	++ blue	dull brownish yellow or straw yellow	++ blue	Siphula ceratites	chromone
porphyrilic acid	5	9	11	26	+ or faint	colourless to very pale greyish	-	Haematomma ochroleucum, Cladonia diversa (some)	dibenzofurane; spot is characteristically obovate
protocetraric acid	5	3	19	27	-	grey	-	Flavoparmelia caperata; Ramalina farinacea and R. siliquosa (PD +, K – chemotypes)	β-orcinol depsidone
caperatic acid	6	4	32	25	-	-	-	Flavoparmelia caperata, Platismatia glauca	fatty acid; said to drag protocetraric acid upwards in Parmelia caperata
pulvinic acid	7	9	42	37	++ orange	pale, fading	+ pale or dulled	Pseudocyphellaria aurata, P. crocata	pulvinic acid derivative; yellow pigment
fumarprotocetraric acid	7	1	26	36	-	grey	-	Cladonia ciliata, C. coniocraea, C. pyxidata	β-orcinol depsidone; above protocetraric acid in G
succinprotocetraric	10	4	18	32	-	grey	-	Pertusaria aspergilla	β-orcinol depsidone; separate from fumarprotocetraric in G
pannaric acid	10	5	23	35	+ blue	very pale greyish	dark purple or quenching	Lepraria membranacea	dibenzofurane; short wave UV + (before heating)

Appendix 1 (continued). TLC data for commonly encountered lichen substances

COMPOUND	RELATIVE Rf C	A	B	G	UV BEFORE HEATING	SPOT COLOUR AFTER ACID AND HEATING	UV AFTER HEATING	SUGGESTED CONTROL SPECIES	NOTES
cryptostictic acid	10	14	10	27	-	orange	-	Parmotrema crinitum, P. perlatum (traces)	β-orcinol depsidone; stictic acid chemosyndrome, separate from PCr-4 in A, or use 2-way TLC
aspicilin	11	53	14	28	-	-	-	Aspicilia calcarea	fatty acid; UV + lilac after heating according to some
echinocarpic acid	11	11	27	32	+ orange	orange to deep orange	+ pale orange	Hypotrachyna endochlora (some)	benzyldepside.
menegazziaic acid	12	19	14	35	-	dull grey-brown	-	Parmotrema crinitum, P. perlatum, Menegazzia terebrata (minor in all)	β-orcinol depsidone; just above stictic acid in G
2'-O-demethylpsoromic acid	12	15	39	46	-	dull yellow-brown	+ dull greenish yellow	Squamarina cartilaginea (chemotype), Peterjamesia circumscripta	β-orcinol depsidone; always with psoromic acid
hiascic acid	12	18	8	47	-	orange	-	Cetrariella delisei	orcinol para-depside; very pale pinkish spot before heating
thamnolic acid	13	3	21	38	-	orange-yellow to orange, or brown in A	-	Cladonia parasitica, C. polydactyla, Pertusaria corallina, Ophioparma ventosa	β-orcinol meta-depside
3-hydroxyphysodic acid	13	15	34	46	-	pinkish brown to pale grey-brown	-	Hypogymnia physodes, H. tubulosa, Pseudevernia furfuracea var. furfuracea	orcinol depsidone; faint yellow pigment on plate
arthoniaic acid	13	31		44	-	very pale pinkish buff	++ blue-violet	Arthonia pruinata	orcinol para-depside
diploschistesic acid	13	21	37		-	yellow-orange	+ dull brown with green halo	Diploschistes muscorum, D. scruposus (some only)	orcinol para-depside; occurs with lecanoric acid; seems difficult to separate, despite different Rf mentioned in literature; use barium hydroxide spot test
variolaric acid	14	18	12	35	-	almost colourless to yellowish or orange-brown	-	Ochrolechia parella, O. microstictoides, Pertusaria lactea	orcinol depsidone
pannaric acid 6-methyl ester	17	23	33	46	+ bluish	very pale greyish	centre ++ blue	Lepraria vouauxii (major)	dibenzofurane; short wave UV + (before heating)
α-alectoronic acid	17	33	31	53	++ white or blue	almost colourless	faint bluish	Arctoparmelia incurva, Cetrelia olivetorum (race), Pertusaria xanthostoma	orcinol depsidone
stictic acid	18	32	9	34	-	orange	orange	Parmotrema perlatum, X. conspersa, Lepraria lobificans	β-orcinol depsidone; usually with several accessories, such as constictic acid
physodic acid	18	25	35	54	- or faint violet	colourless (pale orange pink after some days)	- or blue-black	Hypogymnia physodes, H. tubulosa	orcinol depsidone

Appendix 1 (continued). TLC data for commonly encountered lichen substances

COMPOUND	RELATIVE Rf				UV BEFORE HEATING	SPOT COLOUR AFTER ACID AND HEATING	UV AFTER HEATING	SUGGESTED CONTROL SPECIES	NOTES
	C	A	B	G					
galbinic acid	19	29	17	50	-	bright orange-yellow	dark brown	Myelochroa galbina (N. America, E. Asia)	β-orcinol depsidone
physodalic acid	19	10	33	48	-	dark grey	- or quenching; greenish halo in B	Pertusaria multipuncta, Hypogymnia physodes	β-orcinol depsidone
haemoventosin	20	38	2	35	- (purplish)	red-purple		Ophioparma ventosa (apothecia)	naphthaquinone; red pigment
hypoprotocetraric acid	22	22	37	48	+ whitish	pale yellow with pale orange halo	+ bluish with dark brown halo	Ramalina siliquosa (race), R. farinacea (race)	β-orcinol depsidone
lecanoric	22	28	44	54	-	yellow-orange	+ dull green with brown halo	Melanelixia fuliginosa, Punctelia subrudecta, Pertusaria hemisphaerica	orcinol para-despide; separate from gyrophoric acid in EA or by microcrystal test
strepsilin	23	39	26	45	-	pale orange	- or + orange	Cladonia strepsilis	dibenzofurane
skyrin	23	37	35	60	+ orange or golden-yellow	dirty yellow or brownish to pink-grey	-	Phaeophyscia orbicularis (some), P. endococcina, P. endophoenicea	bis-anthraquinone; yellow pigment, K + purple; (yellow to orange in thallus)
murolic acid	24	23	27		-	-	-	Lecanora muralis, Usnea hirta	fatty acid; i+J72n complex of several compounds
lepraric acid	24	25	8	29	- (orangey)	pale pink with yellowish centre	-	Lecanactis latebrarum, Roccella fuciformis	chromone
gyrophoric acid	24	24	42	54	-	orange	+ dull green with brown halo	Ochrolechia androgyna, Hypotrachyna revoluta, Punctelia borreri, Placopsis lambii	orcinol para-despide; separate from lecanoric acid in EA or by microcrystal test
olivetoric acid	25	29	39	57	-	orange	+ pale blue; + red-brown halo in B	Pseudevernia furfuracea var. ceratea, Cetrelia olivetorum (race)	orcinol para-despide; C + red
barbatolic acid	26	9	52	45	-	colourless to pale brown or pinkish	-	Allantoparmelia alpicola (minor), Alectoria nigricans (minor)	benzyldepside; with alectorialic acid and unknown accessories
4-O-methylcryptochlorophaeic acid	27	32	18	84	-	pink	-	Cladonia chlorophaea (race)	orcinol meta-despide; with merochlorophaeic acid
squamatic acid	28	13	23	39	++ blue	pale orange, or bluish in A	+ yellow-orange	Cladonia squamosa var. squamosa	β-orcinol para-despide; short wave UV + (before heating)
secalonic acid A	28	39	13	37	dark red-orange or quenching	pinkish-grey, turning pale yellow or beige	quenching	Hypotrachyna endochlora	bis-xanthone; yellow pigment
5-O-methylhiascic acid	29	21	36	54	-	orange	-	Placopsis lambii, Placynthiella icmalea	orcinol para-depside; separate from gyrophoric acid in C; occurs above gyrophoric acid

Appendix 1 (continued). TLC data for commonly encountered lichen substances

COMPOUND	RELATIVE Rf				UV BEFORE HEATING	SPOT COLOUR AFTER ACID AND HEATING	UV AFTER HEATING	SUGGESTED CONTROL SPECIES	NOTES
	C	A	B	G					
cyathomorpha-unknown	29	19		48	-	grey	-	Cladonia cyathomorpha	probably β-orcinol depsidone; PD + red
nordivaricatic acid	29	33	52	58	-	orange	greenish brown	Lepraria crassissima	orcinol *para*-depside; C + red
norstictic acid	30	40	32	57	-	bright yellow	-	Pleurosticta acetabulum, Xanthoparmelia conspersa, Phlyctis argena	β-orcinol depsidone; K + yellow turning red (with crystals)
norrangiformic acid	30		36	26	-	-	-	Cladonia rangiformis (minor)	fatty acid; satellite of rangiformic acid
unknown	30			57	-	brown in G, pale buff in C; dull mauve in 2 hours	+ pinkish or faint buff	Ropalospora lugubris	occurs with unknown compound of lower Rf
norobtusatic acid	30	27	48	52	-	pale yellow	+ pale green	Hypotrachyna endochlora (major), H. laevigata (minor)	β-orcinol *para*-depside
2'-O-methylnorobtusatic acid	30	27	48	48	-	yellow		Pseudocyphellaria norvegica	β-orcinol *para*-depside
hypostictic acid	32	50	32	58	-	red (pinkish as trace)	++ orange-pink	Parmotrema crinitum, P. perlatum (traces)	β-orcinol depsidone
allopertusaric acid	32	37	33		-	colourless	-	Pertusaria albescens	fatty acid; with (-)-dihydropertusaric acid and others; spot pale pink-brown according to some
alectorialic acid	32	36	50	62	faint: pale brownish	orange-pink with brownish centre	-	Alectoria nigricans, Allantoparmelia alpicola, Buellia pulverea, Fuscidea praeruptorum, Lepraria eburnea, L. neglecta	benzyldepside; turns herbarium paper pinkish brown after several years. KC + pink
rangiformic acid	33	29	41	38	-	-	-	Cladonia rangiformis	fatty acid; identical in TLC to jackinic acid
jackinic acid	33	29	41	38	-	-	-	Lepraria jackii	fatty acid; identical in TLC to rangiformic acid; often with roccellic acid in L. jackii
4-O-demethylplanaic acid	33	42	29	50	-	orange	- (dark orange brown)	Lecidea lithophila (major), L. plana (minor)	orcinol *para*-depside
glomellic acid	33	34	27	57	+	colourless	+ blue	Xanthoparmelia loxodes, X. delisei	orcinol *para*-depside
isoarthothelin	34	45	44	59	+ red	pale dirty pink	+ dark purple	Pyrrhospora quernea, Lecidella asema (race: very common in British Isles), L. meiococca	xanthone; pale yellow pigment, KC + orange
α-collatolic acid	35	40	35	65	+ white	almost colourless	faint bluish	Cetrelia olivetorum (race), Lecanora sulphurea, Tephromela atra	orcinol depsidone
2'-O-methylnorbarbatic acid	36	39	54	51		yellow		Pseudocyphellaria norvegica	β-orcinol *para*-depside
(-)-dihydropertusaric acid	35	42	36		-	-	-	Pertusaria albescens	fatty acid; visible in UV on untreated plates according to some

Appendix 1 (continued). TLC data for commonly encountered lichen substances

COMPOUND	RELATIVE Rf C	A	B	G	UV BEFORE HEATING	SPOT COLOUR AFTER ACID AND HEATING	UV AFTER HEATING	SUGGESTED CONTROL SPECIES	NOTES
2'-O-methylmicrophyllinic acid	36	41	19	52	-	colourless	+++ blue	Porpidia cinereoatra, P. tuberculosa, Enterographa crassa (minor in all),	orcinol *para*-depside; accessory to confluentic acid
picrolichenic acid	36	38	45	59	-	very pale greyish	-	Pertusaria amara, P. melanochlora	orcinol depsone; upper of two similar spots in G in P. amara
teloschistin	36	44	31		+ yellow-orange	yellow	+ yellow-orange	Xanthoria calcicola (trace)	anthraquinone; difficult to confirm by TLC
4-O-demethylbarbatic acid	36	39	54	58	+ blue-grey	pale yellow	+ blue-grey with pale orange halo	Hypotrachyna laevigata (major, with barbatic acid), Cladonia floerkeana (trace)	β-orcinol *para*-depside
protolichesterinic acid	37	35	46	56	-	-	-	Cetraria islandica	fatty acid
cryptochlorophaeic acid	37	46	45	60	+ faint	darkish orange with dull purple-pink halo	-	Cladonia chlorophaea (race)	orcinol *meta*-depside; spot is darker than perlatolic acid
2'-O-methylanziaic	37	42		57	-	orange-yellow with pale halo	+ orange	Lecidea diducens	orcinol *para*-depside
arthothelin	37	43	40	61	+ red	pale dirty pink	+ dull red	Lecanora expallens, Lecidella scabra (race; frequent in British Isles)	xanthone; pale yellow pigment, KC + orange
lobaric acid	38	30	47	62		colourless to pale grey-green	+ blue	Stereocaulon evolutum, Parmelia omphalodes, Protoparmelia badia	orcinol depsidone; KC + violet (extract on filter paper)
notatic acid	38	24	44	55		pale yellow with grey halo	violet with purple halo	Xanthoparmelia notata (Australasia)	β-orcinol depsidone
virensic acid	40	26	56	56	-	grey-black (indigo-blue in A, G), streaking	orange brown to dark brown-black	Sulcaria virens (Asia)	β-orcinol depsidone
unknown	40	42		54	+ faint grey	pink	-	Lepraria diffusa (some)	often present
psoromic acid	41	36	46	59	+ greyish	pinkish or reddish brown, dull brown after a day or more	- or brown	Squamarina cartilaginea (race), Peterjamesia circumscripta, Lecanora muralis	β-orcinol depsidone
norsolorinic acid	41	55	66	84	++ orange	orange	faint pinkish brown	Solorina crocea	anthraquinone; orange pigment (major substance in at least some S. crocea)
baeomycesic acid	42	39	41	56	+ faint buff	orange	++ orange	Dibaeis baeomyces	β-orcinol *para*-depside
sordidone	42	59	42	70	+ faint orange-brown	very pale grey-brown	- or faint brown	Lecanora carpinea, L. rupicola	chromone
nephrosteranic acid	42			58	-	-	-	Lepraria rigidula, Nephromopsis endocrocea (E. Asia)	fatty acid

Appendix 1 (continued). TLC data for commonly encountered lichen substances

COMPOUND	RELATIVE Rf C	A	B	G	UV BEFORE HEATING	SPOT COLOUR AFTER ACID AND HEATING	UV AFTER HEATING	SUGGESTED CONTROL SPECIES	NOTES
zeorin	43	52	43	52	-	dull purple	pink	Haematomma ochroleucum, Cladonia diversa, Lepraria incana	triterpenoid
elatinic acid	43	32	25	56	-	orange	-	Loxospora elatina	β-orcinol *para*-depside
methyl gyrophorate	43	52	42	69	-	pale yellow-pink	-	Peltigera hymenina, P. horizontalis, P. leucophlebia	orcinol *para*-depside
lichesterinic acid	43	44	58		-	-	-	Ochrolechia microstictoides	fatty acid; said to be visible in UV
evernic acid	43	38	60	60	-	straw yellow	brownish with ++ dull green-brown halo	Evernia prunastri	orcinol *para*-depside
2'-O-methylsuperphyllinic acid	44	43	32	59		colourless	+++ blue	Porpidia rugosa (major)	orcinol *para*-depside
miriquidic acid	44	42	46	64	-	green	+++ greenish yellow with red halo	Miriquidica leucophaea	orcinol *para*-depside
grayanic acid	44	38	59	71	++ blue-white	pale straw, no halo	+ faint blue-violet with dark halo	Cladonia callosa, Cladonia chlorophaea (race: rare in British Isles)	orcinol depsidone; much paler spot than sekikaic acid, perlatolic acid, and sphaerophorin
7-chloroemodin	45	53	56	79	- (dark reddish brown)	orange		Pyrrhospora quernea (apothecia), Nephroma laevigatum, Lasallia papulosa (N. America)	anthraquinone
4-O-methylhypoprotocetraric acid	45	35	51	61		pale yellow with grey halo	dark blue	Xanthoparmelia calvinia, X. competita (both S. Africa), X. notata (Australasia)	β-orcinol depsidone
pycnocarpa-unknown	45	43		62	-	colourless	- or faint	Miriquidica pycnocarpa	
schizopeltic acid	46	42	22	51	-	pale lavender to very pale blue-grey, fading after 2-3 days	+ violet or blue-violet	Schismatomma umbrinum (abundant), Lecanactis abietina	dibenzofurane; short wave UV + (before heating)
confluentic acid	46	48	32	61	-	pale yellow	+ grey-green	Porpidia cinereoatra, P. tuberculosa, Enterographa crassa	orcinol *para*-depside; with 2'-O-methylmicrophyllinic acid (+++ blue) as accessory
2-O-methylsulphurellin	46	44	49	63	-	orange-yellow	- (brownish)	Lecanora jamesii	β-orcinol *para*-depside
toensbergianic acid	46	37	45	42	-	-	-	Lepraria sylvicola, L. toensbergiana	fatty acid
obtusatic acid	47	40	61	63	-	pale yellow	+ pale green	Ramalina obtusata (not British Isles), Hypotrachyna endochlora, H. laevigata (minor)	β-orcinol *para*-depside
thuringione	48	53	58		+ orange	colourless	dull red-purple	Lecidella carpathica	xanthone; faint yellow pigment
roccellic acid	48	42	60	50	-	-	-	Lepraria membranacea, Cliostomum griffithii	fatty acid; indistinguishable from angardianic acid by TLC

Appendix 1 (continued). TLC data for commonly encountered lichen substances

COMPOUND	RELATIVE Rf				UV BEFORE HEATING	SPOT COLOUR AFTER ACID AND HEATING	UV AFTER HEATING	SUGGESTED CONTROL SPECIES	NOTES
	C	A	B	G					
angardianic acid	48	42	60	50	-	-	-	Lepraria caesioalba (races), L. alpina (common race)	fatty acid; by TLC indistinguishable from roccellic acid, which may also occur in L. cacuminum
bourgeanic acid	48	54	62	62	-	-	-	Ramalina lacera, Cladonia conista	fatty acid; distinctive in microcrystal test in GE
phlebic acid B	48	44	42		-	green	+ dull pink with pale blue halo	Peltigera britannica	triterpenoid
thiophanic acid	49	55	52	80	+ dull red	pale dirty pink	+ dull purple	Lecanora expallens, Pyrrhospora quernea	xanthone; pale yellow pigment, KC + orange
meta-scrobiculin	49	64	54	85	-	pinkish orange	-	Lobaria scrobiculata	orcinol meta-depside; with para-scrobiculin (minor compound)
planaic acid	50	47	36	61	-	orange-pink, fading a little after a few hours	-	Lecidea plana (major), L. lithophila (minor),	orcinol meta-depside
glomelliferic acid	50	43	47	63	faint	yellow	faint, grey-brown	Xanthoarmelia loxodes, X. delisei	orcinol para-depside
imbricaric acid	50	42	71	76	-	orange	-	Cetrelia olivetorum (race, with ± perlatolic acid)	orcinol para-depside
diffractaic acid	51	44	55	63	- or + grey	bright yellow with dull orange halo	+ brown with orange-brown halo	Usnea ceratina, Alectoria ochroleuca	β-orcinol para-depside; spot dark brown after 24 hours
divaricatic acid	51	39	68	69	+ faint grey	orange	- (greenish brown)	Ophioparma ventosa, Lepraria incana, Fuscidea kochiana, F. lightfootii	orcinol para-depside
sekikaic acid	51	45	57	72	-	pinkish orange with dull pink halo	-	Cladonia chlorophaea (race: rare in British Isles), Ramalina calicaris (some)	orcinol meta-depside; extracts from Ramalina calicaris should be spotted heavily
chrysophthalma-unknown	51	43		67	- or + faint bluish	yellow with orange-pink halo	++ orange-yellow with orange halo, or pale brownish	Chrysothrix flavovirens	short wave UV faintly + (before heating)
barbatic acid	52	44	67	69	+ blue-grey	pale to bright yellow with dull pinkish or pinkish-orange halo	grey to green-brown with ++ golden yellow-brown to orange halo	Cladonia floerkeana, Hypotrachyna laevigata	β-orcinol para-depside; spot develops dark orange halo after a few days
stenosporic acid	52	44	72	70	faint	(yellow-) orange	- (brown)	Melanelia disjuncta, Xanthoparmelia pulla	orcinol para-depside; in P. disjuncta with perlatolic acid; in P. pulla usually major, with divaricatic acid, but sometimes minor
micareic acid	52	44	69	74	+ blue-violet	yellow	+ blue	Micarea prasina	diphenylether; short wave UV + (before heating)
didymic acid	52	44	68	75	+ whitish	± colourless	+ faint blue-violet	Cladonia incrassata (race)	dibenzofurane; see also the potassium ferricyanide spot test

Appendix 1 (continued). TLC data for commonly encountered lichen substances

COMPOUND	RELATIVE Rf				UV BEFORE HEATING	SPOT COLOUR AFTER ACID AND HEATING	UV AFTER HEATING	SUGGESTED CONTROL SPECIES	NOTES
	C	A	B	G					
lesdainin	53	62	56	69	-	purple	++ pink	Botryolepraria lesdainii	triterpenoid
2'-O-methylperlatolic	53	52	48			pale yellow (when abundant)	purple (when abundant)	Porpidia cinereoatra, P. speirea, P. tuberculosa (minor in all)	orcinol para-depside
merochlorophaeic acid	53	52	50	75	-	dull pink	-	Cladonia ch orophaea (race)	orcinol meta-depside; with 4-O-methylcryptochlorophaeic acid
gangaleoidin	54	64	40	63	+ bluish	pale brown to straw or orange-yellow	brown	Lecanora argentata, L. chlarotera, L. gangaleoides, Lecania baeomma	orcinol depsidone
methoxymicareic acid	54	45	69	75	+ blue	pale dull orange	-	Micarea micrococca	diphenylether
perlatolic acid	54	44	75	80	-	(yellow-) orange	- or very faint (dark brown)	Cladonia portentosa	orcinol para-depside; very similar in TLC to sphaerophorin; known from Cladonia, Cetrelia, Parmelia, Stereocaulon
sphaerophorin	55	45	74	80	+ faint violet	(yellow-) orange	faint (yellow brown, or brown with dull halo, or dull greenish brown)	Sphaerophorus globosus	orcinol para-depside; very similar to perlatolic acid in TLC; known from Sphaerophorus spp. and Cladonia imbricarica (rare: Europe but not British Isles, N. America)
prasinic acid	56	53	80	74	+ whitish	pale lilac-grey	+ faint violet	Micarea subviridescens	orcinol para-depside
homosekikaic acid	56	45	65	80	-	pinkish orange with dull pink halo		Cladonia chlorophaea (race: rare in British Isles), Cladonia rei	orcinol meta-depside
fallacinal	57	62	38	65	+ orange	yellow		Xanthoria calcicola (trace)	anthraquinone; yellow pigment; difficult to confirm by TLC
epanorin	58	68	47	84	++ orange	yellow	+ faint orange	Lecanora epanora	pulvinic acid derivative; yellow pigment; separate from rhizocarpic acid in B
caloploicin	58	65	69	86	-	colourless	-	Fulgensia fulgens	β-orcinol depsidone
thiophaninic acid	60	63	63	83	+ pinkish orange	faint pinkish	+ pinkish	Pertusaria flavicans, P. flavida, P. hymenea (s ot heavily in last)	xanthone
phenarctin	61	66	42	87	- or faint grey-brown	brownish yellow with colourless margin	+ orange-brown	Nephroma arcticum	β-orcinol para-depside; separates from nephroarctin in solvent B
3-dechlorodiploicin	62	58	53	72	-	colourless	-	Diploicia canescens	orcinol depsidone; occurs with diploicin; experimental data suggest below perlatolic acid in C
nephroarctin	63	70	52	87	-	yellow with colourless margin	+ dull orange-brown	Nephroma arcticum	β-orcinol para-depside; separates from phenarctin in solvent B
rhizocarpic acid	65	67	41	84	++ orange	yellow	+ orange	Rhizocarpon geographicum, Psilolechia lucida, Chrysothrix chrysophthalma	pulvinic acid derivative; yellow pigment; separate from epanorin in B

90

Appendix 1 (continued). TLC data for commonly encountered lichen substances

COMPOUND	RELATIVE Rf				UV BEFORE HEATING	SPOT COLOUR AFTER ACID AND HEATING	UV AFTER HEATING	SUGGESTED CONTROL SPECIES	NOTES
	C	A	B	G					
diploicin	67	65	65	84	-	colourless	-	Diploicia canescens (with 3-dechlorodiploicin)	orcinol depsidone
placodiolic acid	67	65	60	85	- (dark reddish)	yellow-brown	faint dark orange-brown	Cyphelium inquinans, Rhizoplaca chrysoleuca (Europe, not British Isles), Buellia arborea	dibenzofurane: usnic acid; in G overlaps with atranorin to produce a purple spot (in same way as usnic acid)
methyl 2'-O-methylmicrophyllinate	69	68	42	80	-	colourless	+++ blue	Porpidia contraponenda (major)	orcinol *para*-depside
usnic acid	71	70	66	88	quenching	very pale yellowish, turning grey-green	-	Cladonia diversa, Flavoparmelia caperata, Xanthoparmelia conspersa	dibenzofurane: usnic acid; pale yellow pigment
2,7-dichlorolichexanthone	73	77	70	70	-	colourless to very pale yellow	-	Lecanora albscens, L. dispersa	xanthone
tenuiorin	76	76	55	90	-	yellow-orange	dull yellow- or brown-green with grey halo	Peltigera hymenina, P. leucophlebia	orcinol *para*-depside
coronatone	88	72	60	88	+ pinkish orange	yellow, soon fading	+ orange	Pertusaria leioplaca, P. pertusa	xanthone
vulpinic acid	76	71	54	88	++ orange to orange-brown	yellow	- or pink with olive brown centre	Chrysothrix chlorina, Letharia vulpina (Europe, not British Isles)	pulvinic acid derivative; yellow pigment
pinastric acid	78	70	55		++ pink-orange	lemon yellow	++ pale pink with orange-brown centre	Cetraria pinastri, Chrysothrix candelaris (race)	pulvinic acid derivative; yellow pigment
isousnic acid	79	75	76		quenching	very pale yellowish, turning grey-green	-	Lecanora flavopunctata (N. Europe, not British Isles), Bunodophoron notatum, B. ramuliferum (Australasia)	dibenzofurane: usnic acid
atranorin	79	75	73	90	-	dull yellow to orange-yellow	dull orange-yellow	Evernia prunastri, Hypogymnia physodes, H. tubulosa, Parmotrema perlatum	β-orcinol *para*-depside; produces purple spot where overlapping with usnic acid on plate
pannarin	79	73	63	88	+ grey	brown, soon dull purple	- or quenching	Pannaria rubiginosa, P. conoplea	β-orcinol depsidone
chloroatranorin	81	74	73	90	- (grey-green)	pale yellow	-	Evernia prunastri, Hypogymnia physodes, H. tubulosa, Pseudevernia furfuracea	β-orcinol *para*-depside; pale yellow pigment; occurs with atranorin, separate in E: well below atranorin on plate
unknown	81	75		91	+ reddish-orange	yellow	+ orange	Trapeliopsis pseudogranulosa	anthraquinone; yellow pigment (on plate), orange in thallus
parietin	82	75	71	89	++ golden yellow	yellow	++ orange-yellow	Xanthoria parietina, X. calcicola	anthraquinone; yellow to orange pigment
fragilin	82	75	67	89	+ dull orange	yellow	+ orange	Fulgensia fulgens	anthraquinone; yellow to orange pigment

Appendix 1 (continued). TLC data for commonly encountered lichen substances

COMPOUND	RELATIVE Rf			UV BEFORE HEATING	SPOT COLOUR AFTER ACID AND HEATING	UV AFTER HEATING	SUGGESTED CONTROL SPECIES	NOTES
	C	A	B	G					
argopsin	82	77	73	92	pale grey	colourless to very pale yellow-brown	grey	Phyllopsora rosei, Micarea leprosula, M. lignaria var. lignaria, Halecania viridescens	β-orcinol depsidone
solorinic acid	85	80	78	92	++ orange	pinkish orange	++ orange or orange-red	Solorina crocea	anthraquinone; pinkish orange pigment (on plate)
calycin	88	78	79	92	quenching	yellow	quenching	Candelariella medians, Pseudocyphellaria aurata	pulvinic acid derivative; yellow pigment
pulvic acid lactone	90	80	82	94	-	yellow	-	Candelariella medians, Pseudocyphellaria aurata	pulvinic acid derivative; yellow pigment

Appendix 2. TLC data for commonly encountered xanthones.

With few exceptions, relative Rf follows Elix & Crook (1992) and Wintabolites (Mieztsch et al. 1994); UV fluorescence based on Leuckert & Knoph (1992) and experimental data. Substances listed according to degree of chlorination and 0-methylation (see Section 9.6.3 for nomenclature of xanthones).

position of Cl	position of OCH3	norlichexanthone (n) or lichexanthone (l)	TRIVIAL NAME	A	B	C	E	F	Approximate order in solvent J (lowest first)	FLUORESCENCE IN LONG-WAVE UV	SUGGESTED CONTROL SPECIES
4,5	-	n		44	48	33	14	49	8	pinkish orange	Lecidella scabra (race: traces with arthothelin)
2,4,5	-	n	arthothelin	43	40	37	5	32	4	dull red to reddish purple	Lecanora expallens[1], Buellia ocellata, Lecanora alboflavida
2,5,7	-	n	isoarthothelin	45	44	36	6	18	3	orange-brown	Pyrrhospora quernea, Lecidella meiococca
4,5,7	-	n	asemone	47	55	37	7	20	4	yellow-orange	Lecidella asema (race)
2,4,5,7	-	n	thiophanic acid	55	52	49	2	9	2	brown to orangey brown	Lecanora expallens, L. confusa, Pyrrhospora quernea
5	3	n	vinetorin	52	57	48	29	69			Lecanora semipallida
4,5	3	n		57	52	58	24			pale orange	Lecidella asema (race: minor)
5,7	3	n	aotearone	67	67	59	16	40	7	bright yellow	Lecidella meiococca (minor), Lecidella asema (race: very common in Britain; minor)
2,4,5	3	n	thuringione	53	58	48	15		9	orange to light orange-brown	Lecidella carpathica, L. scabra (race)
2,5,7	3	n	capistratone	64	56	56	6	16	4	orange brown	Lecidella meiococca, Lecidella asema (race: very common in Britain)
4,5,7	3	n	3-O-methylasemone	66	64	65	11	32	6	bright yellow	Lecidella meiococca (minor), Lecidella asema (race: very common in Britain; minor)
2,4,5,7	3	n	3-O-methylthiophanic acid	65	69	61	3	8	3	orange-brown	Lecidella asema (race: minor)
2,4	6	n	thiophaninic acid	63	63	60	12	40	6	pinkish-orange (in C)	Pertusaria flavicans, P. flavida , P. hymenea (spot heavily in last species)
2,7	6	n		52	46	46	12	44			Lecidella asema (race), L. elaeochroma (race)
2,4,5	6	n	granulosin (6-O-methylarthothelin)	63	56	60	8	36	6	purple	Lecidella elaeochroma (race: common in Britain)
-	3,6	l	lichexanthone	72	66	75	52		10	orange	Lecidella elaeochroma (soralia only), Varicellaria rhodocarpa (Europe: not British Isles)
2,7	3,6	l	2, 7-dichlorolichexanthone	77	70	80	24	57	10	dull reddish purple	Lecanora albescens, L. dispersa

93

Appendix 2 (continued). TLC data for commonly encountered xanthones.

position of Cl	position of OCH3	norlichexanthone (n) or lichexanthone (l)	COMPOUND TRIVIAL NAME	RELATIVE Rf A	B	C	E	F	Approximate order in solvent J (lowest first)	FLUORESCENCE IN LONG-WAVE UV	SUGGESTED CONTROL SPECIES
4,5	3,6	l	coronatone	72	60	76	43	77	10		Pertusaria coronata, P. leioplaca, P. pertusa
			conferta-unknown 1			32			4	dull reddish brown to purple-red	Lecanora conferta auct. (with c. 2 other xanthones visible in solvent J)
			confusa-unknown			25			1	dark orangey brown	Lecanora confusa, L. expallens

[1] The compound in this species is similar to arthothelin in Rf, but differs slightly in fluorescence, and may prove to be a different substance.

Appendix 3. Hazard data for reagents mentioned in this book.

Compiled from various sources. For explanation of overall hazard group, see text. Data on hazards is continually updated, always check manufacturer's data.

Risk Phrases - CONTINUED ON FOLLOWING PAGES

Risk phrase key:

- R8: Contact with combustible material may cause fire
- R10: Flammable
- R11: Highly flammable
- R12: Extremely flammable
- R14: Reacts violently with water
- R19: May form explosive peroxides
- R20: Harmful by inhalation
- R21: Harmful in contact with skin
- R22: Harmful if swallowed
- R23: Toxic by inhalation
- R24: Toxic in contact with skin
- R25: Toxic if swallowed
- R31: Contact with acids liberates toxic gas
- R34: Causes burns
- R35: Causes severe burns
- R36: Irritating to eyes
- R37: Irritating to respiratory system

SOLVENTS

Solvent	OVERALL HAZARD GROUP	PHYSICO-CHEMICAL DANGERS	HEALTH AND ENVIRONMENTAL DANGERS	R8	R10	R11	R12	R14	R19	R20	R21	R22	R23	R24	R25	R31	R34	R35	R36	R37
acetic anhydride	B, S		Harmful, Corrosive		10												34			
acetone	C, S	Highly flammable	Irritant			11													36	37
butanol	C, S		Harmful, Irritant		10					20	21	22								37
chloroform	E, S		Harmful, Irritant							20		22							36	37
cyclohexane	C, S	Highly flammable	Harmful, Irritant, Dangerous for the environment			11				20									36	37
dichloromethane	E, S		Harmful																36	
diethyl ether	B, S	Extremely flammable	Harmful				12		19	20	21	22							36	37
1,4-dioxane	E, S	Highly flammable	Harmful, Irritant			11			19	20	21	22							36	

Appendix 3 (continued). Hazard data for reagents mentioned in this book: Risk Phrases R8 to R37

Reagent	Disposal	Classification	10	11	14	20	21	22	23	24	25	34	35	36	37
ethyl acetate	C, S	Highly flammable / Irritant		11										36	37
hexane	D, S	Highly flammable / Harmful		11		20								36	37
Industrial Methylated Spirit	C, S	Highly flammable / Toxic							23	24	25			36	37
methanol	C, S	Highly flammable / Toxic		11					23	24	25			36	
methyl *tert*-butyl ether	D, S	Highly flammable / Harmful		11										36	37
methyl ethyl ketone (2-butanone)	C, S	Highly flammable / Irritant		11										36	37
toluene	C, S	Highly flammable / Harmful		11		20			23	24	25			36	37
OTHERS															
acetic acid, glacial	C, S	Corrosive	10				21						35		
ammonia solution (0.88 SG)	C, S	Toxic, Corrosive, Dangerous for the environment	10					22	23			34			
aniline	D, S	Toxic, Dangerous for the environment				20	21	22	23	24	25			36	37
barium hydroxide	C, S	Harmful							23	24	25	34		36	
boric acid	D, S	Harmful												36	37
calcium chloride	C, S	Irritant						22						36	37
chloral hydrate	C, S	Toxic									25			36	
Chlorazol Black	E	Harmful													
Congo Red	E	Harmful			14										
N, N-diethyl-1,4-phenylenediamine	C, S	Toxic				20	21		23	24	25	34		36	37
erythrosin	B							22							
ferric chloride	C, S					20	21	22				34			
formic acid	E, S	Corrosive						22					35		
glycerol	A, S													36	
hydrochloric acid (concentrated)	C, S	Toxic, Corrosive							23			34		36	37
iodine	D, S	Harmful, Dangerous for the Environment				20	21			24	25	34			
lactic acid	C, S											34			

Appendix 3 (continued). Hazard data for reagents mentioned in this book: Risk Phrases R8 to R37

Reagent	A		8	11	14	20	21	22	23	24	25	31	34	35	36	37
magnesium acetate tetrahydrate	A															
MBTH	E, S	Harmful				20	21	22							36	37
nitric acid (concentrated)	C, S	Oxidizing agent; Corrosive	8		14				23	24	25			35		
phenol	C, S	Toxic, Corrosive							23	24	25		34			
para-phenylenediamine	D, S	Toxic, Dangerous to the environment							23	24	25				36	37
potassium carbonate	B, S					20	21	22								
potassium ferricyanide	B, S					20	21	22								
potassium hydroxide	C, S	Corrosive			14	20	21	22					34	35*		
potassium iodide	E, S														36	
pyridine	B, S	Highly flammable; Harmful		11		20	21	22								
quinoline	D, S	Harmful, Dangerous to the environment				20	21	22							36	37
silver nitrate	D, S	Corrosive	8					22					34			
sodium hypochlorite solution (domestic bleach)	C, S		8									31	34		36	37
sodium sulphite	D, S							22							36	
sulphuric acid (concentrated)	C, S	Corrosive			14				23					35		
o-toluidine	E, S	Toxic, Dangerous to the environment							23	24	25				36	37
Toluidine Blue	A															
triethylamine	C, S	Highly flammable; Harmful, Corrosive		11		20	21	22					34	35		
zinc chloride	D, S	Corrosive						22					34			

Risk Phrases - CONTINUED FROM PRECEDING PAGES

Risk phrase	Code	acetic anhydride	acetone	butanol	chloroform	cyclohexane	dichloromethane	diethyl ether	1,4-dioxane	ethyl acetate	hexane	Industrial Methylated Spirit
Irritating to skin	R38		38	38	38	38	38	38	38	38	38	38
Possible risks of irreversible effects	R40				40		40		40			
Risk of serious damage to eyes	R41	41		41								41
May cause sensitization by skin contact	R43											
May cause cancer	R45				45		45		45			
May cause heritable genetic damage	R46				46				46			
Danger of serious damage to health by prolonged exposure	R48				48						48	
May cause cancer by inhalation	R49											
Very toxic to aquatic organisms	R50											
May cause harm to the unborn child	R61											
Possible risk of impaired fertility	R62										62	
Possible risk of harm to the unborn child	R63							63				
Harmful, may cause lung damage if swallowed	R65					65						
Repeated exposure may cause skin dryness or cracking	R66			66				66		66		
Vapours may cause drowsiness and dizziness	R67		67			67		67		67		
Toxic: danger of very serious irreversible effects through inhalation, in contact with skin and if swallowed	R39/23/24/25											39/23/24/25
May cause sensitization by inhalation and skin contact	R42/43											
Very toxic to aquatic organisms, may cause long-term adverse effects in the aquatic environment	R50/53					50/53						

notes

Appendix 3 (continued). Hazard data for reagents mentioned in this book: Risk Phrases R38 onwards

Reagent	38	40	41	45	48	50	61	62	63	39/23/24/25	42/43	Notes
methanol	38											
methyl *tert*-butyl ether	38	40										
methyl ethyl ketone (2-butanone)	38		41									
toluene												
OTHERS												
acetic acid, glacial												
ammonia solution (0.88 SG)						50						
aniline	38	40	41		48	50						
barium hydroxide												
boric acid	38							62				
calcium chloride	38											
chloral hydrate	38											
Chlorazol Black				45					63			
Congo Red				45					63			
N, N-diethyl-1,4-phenylenediamine	38											
erythrosin												
ferric chloride												
formic acid											42/43	
glycerol	38											
hydrochloric acid (concentrated)												
iodine						50	61				42/43	
lactic acid												
magnesium acetate tetrahydrate												
MBTH	38	40										
nitric acid (concentrated)												
phenol												Very minor skin contact may result in sufficient material absorbed to cause death

Appendix 3 (continued). Hazard data for reagents mentioned in this book: Risk Phrases R38 onwards.

para-phenylenediamine	38	40		43							42/43	50/53	
potassium carbonate													
potassium ferricyanide													
potassium hydroxide													
potassium iodide	38								61		42/43		
pyridine													
quinoline	38	40	41										
silver nitrate		40											
sodium hypochlorite solution (domestic bleach)	38												
sodium sulphite	38	40											
sulphuric acid (concentrated)							49						Never add water - dilute by carefully adding acid to a larger quantity of water
o-toluidine	38				45	46		50					
Toluidine Blue													
triethylamine													
zinc chloride										63			

Appendix 4. Alternative names of lichen substances mentioned in this book

The following list gives a short selection of alternative names for lichen substances, which have been used in recent years.

name used in this book	other names
confumarprotocetraric acid	Cph-2
lesdainin	6α-acetoxyhopan-22-ol
2-O-methylsulphurellin	3,5-dichloro-4-O-demethylplanaic acid
4-oxypannaric acid 2-methyl ester	'oxypannaric acid', 9-methyl 4-hydroxypannarate
pannaric acid 6-methyl ester	'methyl pannaric acid', 15-methyl pannarate
parietin	physcion
placodiolic acid	(-)-placodiolic acid
prasinic acid	superlatolic acid
secalonic acid A	entothein
skyrin	rhodophyscin
teloschistin	fallacinol